ONE MORE TIME—
ONE LAST ADVENTURE

"Why'd you come back, Robin?"

"Not to fight."

"Still," said Little John, "it would be something, wouldn't it?"

"To do it one more time?"

Little John nodded. Robin didn't move at all. He merely looked into the fire.

"One more time . . ."

Columbia Pictures and Rastar presents

Audrey
Sean   Hepburn   Robert
Connery   Shaw

ROBIN AND MARIAN

A Richard Lester film

Nicol Williamson

Denholm Elliott   Ronnie Barker
Kenneth Haigh   Ian Holm

and Richard Harris as
Richard the Lionheart

A Ray Stark/Richard Shepherd Production

Music by	John Barry
Executive Producer	Richard Shepherd
Written by	James Goldman
Produced by	Denis O'Dell
Directed by	Richard Lester

Robin and Marian

An Original Screenplay by
JAMES GOLDMAN

With an Introduction by the Author

BANTAM BOOKS · TORONTO · NEW YORK · LONDON

ROBIN AND MARIAN
A Bantam Book / April 1976

Illustration of "Robin Hood" and "Maid Marian" by
Louis Rhead from *Bold Robin Hood and His Outlaw
Band,* penned and pictured by Louis Rhead. Copyright,
1912 by Harper & Row, Publishers, Inc. By permission
of the publisher.

Published simultaneously in the United States and Canada

*Bantam Books are published by Bantam Books, Inc. Its trade-
mark, consisting of the words "Bantam Books" and the
portrayal of a bantam, is registered in the United States
Patent Office and in other countries. Marca Registrada. Bantam
Books, Inc., 666 Fifth Avenue, New York, New York 10019.*

PRINTED IN THE UNITED STATES OF AMERICA

0 9 8 7 6 5 4 3 2 1

This book is dedicated to
Clarence Goldman

Introduction

magine that it's time for reveille and all our current famous figures, fact and fiction, are lining up in the company street. The Sergeant calls them to attention and reads off the roster, all the names. And then, when everyone's accounted for, suppose the Sergeant says: "OK, all heroes will take one pace forward."

Who would move?

It's today, remember; not the 50s or the 30s. If the Sergeant called for antiheroes, we'd see movement in the ranks. But heroes? Men who have High Principles or Noble Dreams, who Risk or Dedicate themselves to Something Better—where did they go?

We used to have them. Take the military hero. He's a year-in-year-out favorite, from Marathon to the Marne. The First World War produced them: Sergeant York or General Pershing, men whose names and deeds we still remember. But in our three wars since, name one. Or politics or sports. Or movies. Imagine Jimmy Stewart today taking on the U.S. Senate and coming out on top. Hilarious; we'd laugh it off the screen.

We don't have heroes at the moment. Why? The answer lies in how they come into being in the first place. Heroes are not born: they're made. By you and me: we make them. Not all the P.R. men or media or schoolbooks in the world can con us into doing it. Consider Lindbergh. People had been up in planes for more than twenty years and all he did was fly to Paris. Compare the importance of this achievement with—and quick, don't think: what was his name?—the first man on the moon.

2

And why don't you and I make heroes anymore? Because we don't believe in them. For precisely the same reason those people have who don't believe in God: lack of empirical evidence. We simply do not find them in the world around us. Who do you know that's noble? Who, among your dinner guests, has risked himself for high ideals? And as for principles, who has them? Who among us would refuse a raise in pay because his moral code was outraged?

Well, some people would. But when we come across them, we explain them away. We're pragmatic people, like the antiheroes we believe in: realistic, practical, tough-minded, cynical. We do what makes sense and, in this light, an act of self-sacrifice is idiotic.

So, when a person does a thing which would have been heroic in another time, we think he's got to be some kind of nut, self-destructive, or he has some angle we don't know about. What's with Ralph Nader anyway? How does he get his kicks? Take any figure who professes an interest in Making Things Better. Pick him from any part of the spectrum, left or right: Martin Luther King or Billy Graham or Pope Paul or Dick Gregory. When confronted with these people, either we suspect them of not believing in their ideals or we discount them as neurotics or we feel suspicious about the ideals themselves.

Put simply, it comes down to this. A hero is someone who performs a heroic action. But if heroic actions don't exist, if they are actually neurotic or self-serving, there can be no heroes. It's as logical as Dr. Pangloss at his best. And just as lunatic. Yet it makes sense to us. We live in a time of doubt, uncertainty, suspicion: of little belief and little faith. And if, like Candide, we should try to cultivate our gardens, we would be stuck with soil in which heroes cannot grow.

In which case, why write another Robin Hood? Why dig him up again? Any man today who robbed the rich to help the poor would either be

3

clapped in the slammer or sent to the funny farm. And, on top of this, to write an adult Robin, to take the man and his legend seriously? I mean, if Robin is for any audience today, he's for the kids; not you and me.

Dead wrong. I think we do believe in all the worn-out things that Robin stands for. I cannot see *Peter Pan*, for instance, without bursting into tears and applause when Tinker Bell asks me to clap if I believe in fairies. This is not, I'm convinced, because I long for lost innocence or a childhood I did not enjoy.

It comes from something absolutely basic to the human spirit. At some point in our lives, sooner or later, all of us who aren't demented find that living without ideals—or principles or beliefs or call them what you will—is intolerable. We must believe in Something. We are driven to it. The reasons stem from what I take to be an instinctive need of the human mind to structure what it experiences. We put things into patterns, we insist on finding repetitions and relationships. We organize what we perceive. We cannot stop doing it.

And when we organize and structure things, the most important question is the Final Cause: what purpose does it serve? Or why? Or what's it for? Life must make sense. There has to be a reason. Not a scientific reason; science never asks this kind of why, it's not a "scientific question." But we ask it and we cannot find the answer in the self. It must be something bigger, larger, more important than our hungers, needs or welfare. The end result does not have to be God but we absolutely must believe in something more than Number One.

In spite of what we think or feel or how we see our world today, we simply cannot live without ideals. We do believe: we're stuck with it. As children, we believed in good and evil, great men, villains, sacrifice, brave deeds, all the stuff of heroes. And we didn't do this just because our parents told us to. It's not conditioning. It's in our souls.

The fact is we love heroes, we believe in heroes, we need heroes: and we feel these things because the stuff of heroes—deny it or disguise it or call it what we will—lives inside every one of us. Which is reason enough, intellectually speaking, to write another Robin Hood.

None of this, of course, has much to do with why I wrote one.

Almost everything I've ever written has a hero and a heroine. I'm drawn to them; they fascinate and move me. There are many reasons why, some of which I know and some of which, the basic ones, are known only to God and my analyst.

To begin with, I was stagestruck as a kid. I grew up with the realistic theater of the 30s and the 40s. The basic play which dominated these years, the vision which began with Rice, O'Neill, Odets and reached its end with Inge and Miller, was fundamentally literal and domestic. The stage was filled with average people, from the Clerk in *The Adding Machine* to the salesman in *The Death of*, sometimes facing little problems, sometimes big ones.

The more I saw of this, the less I liked it. Another kitchen, another tenement or farmhouse; another evening spent with people of narrow interests and limited intelligence whose conversation struck and still strikes me as pretty dull.

Surely there was something more exciting— vivid, unexpected, unfamiliar; something new to put up on the stage. And issues; something else to write about. I mean, if I met Willy Loman in a bar, I wouldn't talk to him for long; he's boring and he's rather disagreeable. And I'm sorry he's a failure but that's all he is. Our System didn't fail; he did.

For a while, I thought the way to something new and better was to be found in the nonrealistic theater of Giraudoux and Annouilh and I wrote a number of shallow, derivative and stillborn plays to prove it. I'm still deeply fond of works like *The Enchanted* and *Ondine*, and I take *Waltz of the Toreadors* to be one of the ten best plays of the century. But it was not a solution that worked for me. Nor has it, in the years since, for our theater.

So by trial and error, neurosis by neurosis, bit by bit, I found myself writing about heroes. It was never a conscious decision; it just happened. The first piece I ever wrote good enough to be spoken by living student actors was a play about Don Juan. The thing is ponderous, the writing purple and it's overloaded with Ideas—but it felt like coming home. And everything I've written since that I can call my own has been dominated by a hero and a heroine.

What is a hero, anyway? What makes him different from the rest of us? It has to do, I think, with his insides, with what the man himself is like. Or woman. With the spirit or the soul. Not with the deed itself but why the deed is done. The soldier who, in battle, risks his life to save another man has done a thing we call heroic; but he may or may not be a hero. It depends on why he did it. Ulysses was a hero; U. S. Grant was not.

Heroes, first of all and most of all, are big. They have size and scope and depth and range and passion and intensity and temperament; or most of the above. They need not be intelligent; it's spirit that is central here, not mind. Socrates was a hero but you can't build a case for Immanuel Kant.

People with this kind of stuff inside are almost invariably driven to Do Something. They live at a high level of intensity and their feelings or passions demand release or expression in action of some kind. Whatever form the action takes, it has the same size and intensity as the pressures that produced it. To put it plainly, at the risk of sounding dumb, heroes are big people who do big things in a big way.

Which brings us to one more reason why contemporary heroes are so hard to find. We conceive of ourselves as small. If you've ever stood in the entrance of a nineteenth-century mansion, you know what I mean. The kind of man who felt he could fill all that space was of a very different size than those of us to go to work in skyscrapers.

To be less fanciful about it, men of the Enlightenment believed that knowledge was finite and knowable. A nineteenth-century scientist felt sure that Nature could be mastered and controlled. A citizen at a town meeting felt, with reason, that his voice was audible.

Today, we know better; or worse. Nature is out of control, our votes mean nothing, God, who put Man in the center of the universe, is on the side-lines. Even what we see and feel is doubtful, thanks to Freud. We think in billions and we take ourselves to be just one more unit in a mass. We're numbered, we're computed and without a *carte d'identité*, who are we?

It is for this reason, and not because I am a history nut, that most of my heroes live in the past. If I tell you a story that happened a long time ago, it's as if the first words on the page were "Once upon a time . . ." The result is a suspension of disbelief, and things we could not swallow in the here and now—great men and noble deeds—seem real and true to us again.

We've had a lot of heroes in the last three thousand years. Why, out of all these great and mighty men, choose Robin Hood? I could, and shortly will, produce a number of reasons; but the fact of the matter is, I didn't choose him at all. He presented himself. He more or less demanded to be written. That may sound a little fey. It's not.

It is the only way a writer knows—or thinks he knows—that an idea has life inside. A figure or a subject or a situation pops into your consciousness and gives you physical reactions: heart thumps, stomach knots, cold hands, the sweats, whatever. And what you think, in one phrase or another, is, "Ohmygod, I've got one."

What is there about Robin Hood, about the legend, capable of giving a grown man the sweats? Plenty. Robin's legend, after that of Arthur and his Knights, is one of the oldest in our language; and, surpassing Arthur's, the most widely known and popular. In fact, in a recent survey conducted to determine the most famous figures of fact or fiction, Robin's name came second on the list, just after Jesus.

People have been telling Robin stories and singing Robin songs since, give or take a bit, 1200. Many of these ballads still exist and the Robin they present has many things in common with the legend we're familiar with. He was an outlaw and he did live in a forest with a band of men. He was the leader and the bravest and the keenest marksman, all of that.

He was not, however, the Robin of the Flynn or Fairbanks movies or the book by Howard Pyle that most of us grew up with. He was not of noble birth. He did not spit in Prince John's eye or save the throne of England for its rightful occupant, King Richard. Nor, while he robbed the rich, was he much known for passing on the proceeds to the poor.

On the whole, the Robin of the ballads had adventures of two kinds. In one—he was alone for these—he'd meet a fellow in the woods. Whoever this fellow was—a cooper or a pinder or a miller or a farmer—he was always basically the same: hale, hearty, brave. A stout fellow. The two would greet each other, banter back and forth a while and then a challenge would be made. A friendly, not-so-friendly fight with swords or quarterstaffs or fists.

The fight would last most of the day. And at the end of this mindless biffing around, Robin's pate would be sorely split and the miller or whoever would be equally laid out. At this point, Robin generally says: "You are a decent fellow and I like you. Come with me to my camp and we will eat and drink and in the morning, you go on your way." And they would.

Judging by the number of ballads that tell this story, it was extremely popular and very satisfying. What it essentially seems to be saying is Robin meets an equal—but not quite an equal since the fight was with one weapon only—and does honor to this man by taking him home and having a good time.

The other kind of adventure is armed robbery. Robin, sometimes alone and sometimes in the com-

ROBIN HOOD

Courtesy of *The Bettman Archive*

pany of Little John and others, comes across a person traveling on a road that passes through the forest. This person is invariably both rich and despicable; that is to say, either a merchant or a higher clergyman.

Again, there is some bantering. In general, the bishop lies about his wealth: he hasn't any or he won't tell where he's hidden it. Robin always finds the gold, the coins, the jewels, whatever. Then he takes the bishop to his camp and makes a fool of him before his men. The bishop is made to dance or sing songs; or his clothes are taken from him; or he's hung upside down from a tree for a while.

And then, when Robin and his men have had their sport, the bishop is treated exactly as the miller was. He is given food and drink and released in the morning. Minus his riches, of course. Little is ever said about what happens to the riches. There are some ballads in which Robin helps people who have been abused by Authority, returning to the individual concerned what has been unjustly taken from him; but I can't recall anything which describes Robin as a charitable institution.

It is essentially these two stories, told again and again, which comprise the historical Robin. Over the centuries, the legend has been subject to change; to those adjustments or corruptions which increase its appeal to a particular time. But beneath the encrustations is this figure who has lived and been loved because he bonked stout fellows on the head, getting bonked in return, and because he robbed and made fools out of rich and powerful men.

At first glance, it doesn't seem like much to build a legend on. But legends don't survive by accident and implicit in these two stories are the reasons Robin lives for us today.

The Robin-goes-a'bonking stories tell us what kind of man Robin was. They don't look it but they are character sketches. Robin was created by and for the common people of his time and his character is heroic—or big, if you will—because he is the best possible commoner; he embodied, in the

highest degree, those traits the people most admired. He was fair and just and honorable. He loved the Virgin, prayed daily and was deeply religious. He was fearless, he was clever. He loved food and drink and games and jokes. He was unfailingly courteous to women. And as a fighter, he was peerless.

Why, then, when he has his fights with all the various Stout Fellows, does he always get his pate cracked? To keep him in scale. To have a hero who was, at once, both great and like oneself. He was a hero the peasantry could identify with, a thing they could not do with the other great English hero, King Arthur. The Arthurian legend was widely known at the time Robin was invented. But Arthur was a hero for the nobility. He was powerful and rich and civilized; a ruler with a ruler's needs and problems, a figure without meaning to men who had no possessions, no rights and damned little food to eat. But Robin was a man after their own hearts. He was a man without an equal who, in spite of that, met equals every day.

The Robin-robs-a-rich-man stories tell us of our hero in action, of the kind of deed he did. Before all else, Robin was an outlaw. He found the laws unbearable and broke them. But not all laws: only those that cruelly affected the peasantry. And the only men he robbed were those the peasants hated, figures that they dealt with on a daily basis: Sheriffs, Earls and Abbots.

Clearly, Robin was attacking his society. But never with political intent. There was no wish to bring the house down. Remember that the Magna Carta was a product of the same time as Robin. It occurred to the nobility to curb the powers of the King; but not to the common people. The forces that controlled them were too mighty, and instead of striking out, they gave us Robin.

Robin almost never kills. Instead, he wins by laughter. He diminishes the mighty with derision, makes the great men small, reduces them by ridicule and sends them on their way.

Most repressed societies produce such figures, from Till Eulenspiegel down to Schweik. They give us joyful vengeance on the powers that we hate. They give us justice, sweet release. I can, for instance, easily recall the hate I felt for Richard Nixon; years of it and no relief. I'm not a revolutionary or a murderer, I have a reverence for law and I adore my Constitution. But oh, if only Robin had been there to make the man sing Sister Kate as he danced naked in the Rose Garden.

And so it is, I think, why Robin lives and speaks to us.

I had and have, beyond these general feelings, private ones which made me turn to Robin. The Robin that I wrote is both the same and different from the one the ballads sing about. Inside, in spirit and in feeling, he's the same. The difference is exterior: he's old. Not old-old; he's not doddering. But he is close to fifty which, in the first decade of the thirteenth century where I've put him, was a considerable age. And what my story tells is how he falls in love again and fights his greatest fight and dies.

Why tell you such a story? Lots of reasons, most of them emotional. For openers, I have a thing about old heroes. That's to say, about brave men who have achieved great things and who, in spite of knowing that their powers fail, that their old glories are beyond them now, set out again.

There is, by way of example, a poem by Tennyson entitled "Ulysses." When I read it first, some time in my teens, it made me cry. I have never, in the years since, been able to read it without bursting into tears. I am about to quote the end of it to you and, in opening the book to make sure I got it right, it happened to me again.

The poem is a speech that Ulysses is making to the people whose King he is. He is an old man now and he is leaving his son behind to rule his kingdom. His ships are ready in the port, his mariners stand waiting. He speaks to his people about the old days and the things he did. Then, toward the end, Ulysses says:

Come, my friends,
'Tis not too late to seek a newer world.
Push off, and sitting well in order, smite
The sounding furrows; for my purpose holds
To sail beyond the sunset, and the baths
Of all the western stars, until I die.
It may be that the gulfs will wash us down:
It may be we shall touch the Happy Isles,
And see the great Achilles, whom we knew.
Though much is taken, much abides; and
    though
We are not now that strength which in old
    days
Moved earth and heaven; that which we are,
    we are:——
One equal temper of heroic hearts,
Made weak by time and fate, but strong in
    will
To strive, to seek, to find, and not to yield.

Well, I ask you. There Ulysses stands, as great
a hero as the world has known, and old and frail
and well aware of it. He has comfort, safety,
glory, sons, the love of all his people. And yet,
knowing all the risks, the likelihood of death and
failure, off he goes defying Nature, challenging
his years. A man who, loving God, still shakes a
fist in His face.

I wanted Robin to be like Ulysses. Not as wise
or self-aware; nor as conscious of who he is or
what it is he's doing. But the glory of a man who
stands against all circumstance; who will, once
more, be everything he ever was—that's what I
wanted.

That and one thing more. The man must do
what he sets out to do, if only for a moment. The
victory over life that's gnawing at Ulysses has to
happen. If he makes his speech, casts off and has a
heart attack before he leaves the harbor, it's another story; one I had no wish to tell. What I
wanted was a swansong.

The word itself comes from folklore; from the belief that the swan—whose voice, unlike its form, is remarkably unpleasant—bursts into song before it dies. That moment when, in old age and beyond all reason and all odds, a man is once more everything he ever was—that's a swan song.

When I was a kid, I thought Fritz Kreisler was the greatest fiddler in the world. As it happens, I was right; but all that matters is I thought so. The man, as he grew old, still played magnificently. Then—as I recall it, he was over seventy—he was crossing a Manhattan street when he was struck down by a truck. He was expected to die. He didn't. He was certain to be an invalid. He wasn't. But what there was no doubt about was that he'd never play again.

I was brought up in Chicago and it was several months after Kreisler didn't die that he came to play a concert with the Symphony. I got a ticket, God knows how. I was, I don't remember anymore, fourteen or so and I was there when he came out from the wings.

Slowly, walking very slowly on stick legs, he made it to the podium. He stood there, frail and blinking, while everyone on stage and in the house stood up. Then we sat. He tuned his fiddle; faint and scratchy. The orchestra began the *tutti*. It was a concerto by Vitali; student music, difficult but not demanding.

Kreisler stood there through the music. Stood; that's all. No movement and I wondered if he even heard the orchestra. The time was near when he would have to enter. Still no move; and then the entrance came. The chord was held, it seemed to me, forever. Then Kreisler tucked his fiddle up and played and for a little while there was music from a violin more glorious, more simple, pure and joyful than any sounds I have heard since. He died, I think, within the year—and that's a swan song.

They are rare but they do happen. Ben Hogan, after all his bones were broken, coming back to win an Open; Joyce Cary, dying from paralysis a millimeter at a time, sitting in his wheelchair writing comedy; Toscanini, all but senile, suddenly ripping down the walls with Beethoven's Seventh; Sugar Ray Robinson, completely washed up, showing for a round or two what greatness looks like.

There are other reasons, some of them even worth talking about, for writing a Robin in middle-age; the kind of reasons which, unless I've made a terrible mistake, make the difference between an idea and a good idea. But, at bottom, I'd never have written a piece about Robin if I weren't moved to tears by aging heroes and their swan songs.

In addition to being moved by something, a writer also needs to find it meaningful. This sounds painfully obvious but it's not. In fact, most of the art of the last fifty years—novels, statues, paintings, string quartets—has been an exercise in form and style with little if any content. Implicit in every work of art is, or should be, an unspoken sentence from the artist: "Sit down and listen—or look—because I have something to tell you." There must be meaning—which does not mean the work has to be Serious. All successful art begins with and conveys feelings; but an emotion is not an idea. The thing, whatever it is, must be about something.

So what else is there in my Robin worth writing about? Just this: that on top of being an aging hero with a swan song, he falls in love again and dies.

Which brings us to Maid Marian.

Or very nearly.

Robin and Marian came into my life over fifteen years ago. For reasons far beyond recall, I thought they made a subject for a play. Aside from knowing and adoring Errol Flynn in Lincoln green, I was brought up short on realizing that I knew nothing about the legend at all. So I began to read—as a result of which two things happened.

When you write about Robin, you have a certain amount of latitude as to where you place him in time. There is very little data, and you have almost a hundred years to choose from. It was an easy decision because surely, if Robin was the Greatest Hero, it felt right to drop him into the reign of the Greatest Villain. And that, of course, was Evil King John.

Having little knowledge of such things, I began to read about John. Inevitably, there was material about his parents, King Henry II and his wife, Eleanor of Aquitaine. It wasn't long before I learned that Henry, during the later years of his marriage, kept Eleanor locked up in prison, trotting her out for family gatherings at Christmastime. I was riveted. I thought it was at once hilarious and terrible. Which was how, when I had spent a year discovering that Robin didn't work on stage, I came to write *The Lion in Winter*.

The other thing that happened, of course, was that I began to read the ballads. None of them had anything to say about Robin growing old; he seemed to have no middle-age. He was forever young—except for, now and then, brief references to how he died. And I mean brief; a single quatrain at the end of something long.

The reports of his death varied widely as to all details but one: he always died by treachery. No man or force was great enough to kill him; only betrayal by someone he trusted. More often than not, he was poisoned by someone nameless whom he did not know: a doctor-type, some priest or abbess or abbot since, in those days, the clergy did most of the doctoring.

None of this felt interesting or meaningful to me. The kind of death I wanted had to be a part of Robin's life, connected with it, a result of his character and his intentions. Heroes, as we know too well, can be senselessly cut down by lunatics or die by accident. But once Ulysses sets out from the harbor, his death should come because of his

17

dream. Unless, of course, the message that you have to tell me is life has no meaning.

Then, one day, I came across a ballad which I have since been unable to locate. But I remember it. It was short and fragmentary and unlike all the others. What it said was this.

Robin and Little John go away for a very long time. (No word of where they went or why.) They come back old. (No word of why they came.) There is a great battle. (And again, no information as to who they fought or where or why.) In the battle, Robin is sorely wounded. Little John asks if anyone can help. There is an abbess, he is told, who lives not far and who is greatly gifted in the arts of healing. John half-carries Robin to the abbey. He pounds on the abbey door. It opens. The abbess stands there: Marian.

Her medicines are in a tower room. She bids them come. John carries Robin to the chamber, puts him on a narrow bed. Then Marian asks John to stand guard down below lest enemies appear. He goes. She bolts the door. She mixes herbs and medicines and puts the remedy on Robin's wounds. It is a poison and he dies.

It was, and is, the only account I've come across where Robin's death is meaningful. But what exactly is its meaning? Why does Marian kill Robin? As the ballad stands, it must be vengeance. She was loved and then abandoned and she hates the man who left her. Hates him with such passion that, when he appears after God knows how many years away, she drops him on the spot.

I didn't care for that at all. Dark passions, bleak and twisted feelings, don't belong in Robin's world. Sherwood Forest isn't Greece and Marian the Maid is not Medea. Bitterness and loathing, cruelty and revenge are out of character; the people in this legend have a different set of drives. Robin's a Romantic Figure and his story is a Romance.

At which point, everything came clear. If Robin dies, it is for love. If Marian can poison him, her reason has to be because she loves him so. I had a love-death story on my hands, like Romeo or Tristan.

To say "everything came clear" is a little misleading. It sounds either like a vision in the grip of Inspiration, or an intellectual solution to a puzzle. It's neither one.

Among my cherished beliefs is the conviction that our best writers never know what they're writing about. They invariably think they know; it's the only basis on which they can organize their material and what they feel about it. But you have only to read Coleridge or Wordsworth, both of them first-class thinkers, when they analyse the meaning of their own work. In general, they couldn't be more mistaken. You can see what they thought they were writing about—it's always somewhere in the poem—but they either didn't know about or care about what seems to us to be the meaning.

As for inspiration, it's at best a sometime thing and I suspect that when it happens, one is not aware of it; you simply write or paint a lot that day and it comes out well. When things "come clear," it's much more like discovering a thought or impulse or emotion that you knew from the beginning. It was always there, someplace inside your head, this wish to show or do or tell or make me feel a certain thing. And it's a bit like hunting Easter eggs: you lift a corner of the cushion up, and Bingo!

So my swan song turned a corner and became a romance. What kind of romance? Obviously, one of rediscovery, of returning. Robin, in my ballad, comes back home. Why would a man like Robin do a thing like that? Not out of bitterness, defeat or hopelessness; he does not come back home to die or see the old folks one last time. Good reasons, these, and well worth writing about; but with some other lovers, not these two.

Robin is a man of action. He must do things or he isn't Robin anymore. So he may feel regret or rue; or he may feel a fool for having gone away. He may feel that he has wasted time. But that his life's been wasted—never. He is full of hope, of days yet to be lived, of deeds not done. Of a young man's longings deep in middle-age.

And since this is a story of returning and Maid Marian is there, so are the other leading figures of the legend: Friar Tuck, Will Scarlet and the Sheriff. All of them caught up in unfinished business, living out the needs and dreams and drives, all stopped, midstream, by Robin's leaving twenty years before. It's not fresh starts or second chances: who among us doesn't know you can't go home again? No: it has to do with self-completion, with fully turning whatever your circle may be. Feelings of Fate or Destiny: of being both the mover and the moved.

Sad stuff—but comic, too. And not just because Robin and Marian know a joke when they hear one. Comedy, it seems to me, has very little to do with belly laughs or being funny; any more than tears make tragedy. I may weep buckets over Bette Davis in *Dark Victory* and have dry eyes throughout *Macbeth*; but one's a tragic story and the other's merely sad.

And so, the people in this story, in their hearts and in the things they do, are mixtures: sad and funny, wise and foolish, old hands at despair yet full of hope. They stand locked together by their dreams and passions in a drama they create, yet at the same time can't control, all living out the legend of their lives. And you and I—I know I do —will laugh a little, cry a bit and have a thought or two about our heroes, where they've gone, and wouldn't it be wonderful to have them back again.

What All the Singing Was About

he first thing to be said is this: I'm not a scholar.

That's a pretty dim beginning for a history lesson but it does have its advantages. It protects me from ridicule because of all the gaffes and boners I'm about to make. It protects you from the scholar's favorite pastime, telling you a lot more about a subject than you ever wanted to know. But best of all, from where I sit, it lets me have opinions. I can tell you: "This is how it was as far as I'm concerned"—and devil take the niceties of academic judgment.

Courtesy of The Bettman Archive

The subject is Robin Hood. I want to tackle it the way a newsman would: to start with Who and then go on to What, When, Where and, most important, Why.

So, who was Robin Hood? There are two main schools of thought, both of them wrong. One finds his origins in myth and folklore. The other attempts to tie him to specific historical figures.

We have a large variety of myths to choose from. For example, there's a woodland sprite long popular in English folklore named Robin Goodfellow. Essentially what this Robin does is go about in disguise committing practical jokes.

Or, pressing deeper, other scholars see Robin as an offshoot of the Aryan sun-myth. In this view, Robin Hood is Hod, god of the wind. Maid Marian derives from Morgen, a dawn-maiden; and as for Friar Tuck, he comes from Toki, the spirit of frost and snow.

Still others see Robin as an outgrowth of a knavish and unpleasant German elf named Ruprecht. Or, since Robin is a French form of Rob which is short for Robert . . . And so it goes, all going nowhere; because of the mistaken assumption that Robin's name is the key to his origins.

The scholars who hunt for Robin in history have an equally rough time of it. To begin with, there's the evidence of pipe rolls. Pipe rolls are accounts of expenses and activities conducted by sheriffs and other high representatives of the Crown. These rolls began to appear in the middle of the twelfth century and are, in general, our surest source of historical data for the next several hundred years.

Well, it happens that a pipe roll from Yorkshire in the year 1230 makes specific mention of "Robertus Hood fugitivus." Pretty convincing. Except that there are rolls from the reign of Edward II— which is 1307–1327 and, as we shall see, a hundred years too late—which refer to both a "Robyn Hod" and a "Robertus Hood." The only fact the pipe rolls have to tell us is that Robin Hood was not, in those days, a unique name.

There are any number of other historical accounts—Robin was a follower of Simon de Montfort; or Robin was in reality Robert Fitz-Ooth, born in Locksley in 1160 and the rightful Earl of Huntingdon who, unjustly deprived of his domain, became an outlaw. Well, as it happens, Locksley was a fourteenth-century outlaw and not a town, and Huntingdon was not an earldom at the time and anyway the notion that Robin was a nobleman is both impossible and an invention of the seventeenth century. And so it goes.

The truth, I think, lies in between both schools. On the one hand, there are unmistakable elements of myth and folklore in our legend. But legends can, and often do, have real beginnings. Take King Arthur. He was real. Not as the Arthur that we know; he didn't go on quests, there was no Round Table or Launcelot or Guinevere or Modred or the rest. But in fifth-century Somerset, there was a mighty warrior who won great battles. That much we know; and out of this, the way an oyster makes a pearl, the legend grew.

The same, I think, is true of Robin. There were enormous royal forests in twelfth-century England; dense and unexplored and out of bounds to common people. If you went hunting in the King's woods and got caught, you could expect to be blinded or castrated or merely put to death. Because of these restrictions, the woods were thick and rich with game.

Clearly, a farmer would have to be a pretty desperate man before he picked his bow and arrow up and went out poaching. Yet, many went. They risked their lives for food and they had reasons. The conditions under which a peasant lived were dreadful. He owned nothing, literally nothing; not his hovel nor the land he worked nor what he grew with all his labor.

On top of which, though he was not a slave in our nineteenth-century sense, he did not own himself. He was constantly being taken off to fight the endless wars his lord was endlessly waging. He could not marry, move or travel without due permission. Nor did his own children belong to him; they were his lord's to use or trade or do with what he chose.

So there he was, this poor son of a bitch; not a pot to call his own, forever cold and wet—the English climate wasn't made for ragged peasants—always at the whim and mercy of his lord, and permanently hungry. On his table, breakfast, lunch and dinner, what he found was cheese and eggs and bread and water or brown ale. Year in, year out. And just a mile or two away, out in the woods, was venison enough to sink a ship. It added up to

25

an environment, just like our ghettos, perfectly designed to breed the breaking of the law.

Which is how Sherwood Forest came to be so full of outlaws. And outlaws—this is critical—of an unusual kind. For while there were, inevitably, some murderers and cutthroats, on the whole these men were good. Good in the sense that they did nothing which a moral man could call a crime. To leave a home you find unbearable and thereby be-

come a fugitive; to hunt for meat to fill your children's bellies and thereby become a wanted man—good criminals.

These men, of course, formed social groups or, if you'd rather, bands. And being criminals, they robbed. Now, portable wealth in those days was surprisingly rare; the rich were rich primarily in land and men. There were no banks, and if you did have treasure and you traveled, what you did was take it with you. Which is why they zeroed in on wealthy travelers.

Now, as luck would have it, these outlaws didn't have to leave the safety of the woods: the travelers came to them. The main roads in those days were Roman roads. And, unless my memory is wrong, the greatest and most famous Roman road—it's name was Watling Street—cut straight through Sherwood Forest. It was a bit as if the Jersey Turnpike ran through Alcatraz.

What I'm getting at is clear enough, I think. The circumstances and conditions that gave birth to Robin all were real. The details of the legend and the character of Robin and his men—their fundamental decency and sense of justice—all these elements were literal, were there to be observed and felt, existed at the time. And so, I am convinced, did Robin. In the same way that King Arthur did. Not as the legend that we know but as an outlaw, flesh and blood, who led a band of men in Sherwood Forest.

"What is Robin?" probably sounds like a curious question. Suppose I asked, instead, "What is Othello?" Is he a mighty general or a black man in a white man's world or a paradigm of jealousy and mistrust or a murderer or what? Now, it's my belief that the surest way of knowing what a man is lies in examining his actions; what he does. And so I want to take a close look at the things that Robin does. And at the things he doesn't do.

Robin, first and foremost, is an outlaw. He breaks laws; that's what he does. Which laws? The forest laws: he hunts. The civil law: he was a peasant who left his lord, whose property he was. The criminal and moral law: he robs rich merchants and the higher clergy, fights the sheriff, kills his men. Much the same could be said of Dillinger or the Clantons or Charlie Starkweather. But Robin is unlike these people altogether. Why?

In one of the ballads, Robin is giving instructions to Little John. Put roughly into modern English, what he says is:

> Look you do no husbandman harm
> That tills with his plow;
> Nor any good yeoman
> Who walks in the greenwood;
> Nor any knight or squire
> That would be a good fellow:
> These bishops and archbishops,
> These should you beat and bind;
> The High Sheriff of Nottingham,
> Hold him in your mind.

Essentially, it's a Biblical position: the Good shall be protected and rewarded and the Evil shall be punished. Robin, like a god, is both just and punitive. His law is what we wish our law was: fair and honorable and evenhanded.

What's interesting is who he sees as evil. Rich merchants are a natural; covetous and greedy men are never very popular; and in a time when 90-odd percent of the citizenry had literally nothing, they were hated with a passion.

But why the higher clergy? In *Robin and Marian*, there is talk about an interdict. There was one, in the first decade of the thirteenth century. The Archbishop of Canterbury died and an argument developed between King John and the Pope as to who would succeed him. John appointed one man, the Pope another and the monks of Canterbury voted in a third. Three men in the Holy See has always struck me pretty funny but it wasn't funny then. The Church, remember, was a temporal power second in importance to the King. So naturally, everyone got very stubborn and the Pope, using one of his biggest guns, placed England under interdict.

What this meant, in large part, was that Mass could not be said, that burial on holy ground could not be held and that, in general, the daily function of the Church came to a dead stop. Now, the Plantagenets were not much given to religion and King John's foul behavior in church, on those rare occasions he appeared, is legendary. Nor, on the whole, were the nobility believers.

Who minded if the churches closed? The people did. Religion played a role in daily life so vast as to be almost incredible to us today. The village church, the village priests—the core of peasant life revolved around them. A peasant prayed not once but several times a day: and so did Robin. The ballads are full of his devoutness, his devotions, his love—in particular—of the Virgin. From which, the ballads tell us, his respect of women and his role as their protector comes.

What was it, then, with all these bishops and archbishops? Why were they the enemy? Essentially for the same reason that the merchants were. The village priest lived like his villagers; his roof, his food, his clothes were just as poor as theirs. The high clergy both lived like kings and with them: they were noblemen with mitres on. Whatever work it was they did, it wasn't God's. To Robin and the men who wrote and sang his songs, a bishop was as holy as an anti-Christ.

So, think a minute: what is Robin turning into? He stands against the Church. He stands against the State. He takes his stand in Sherwood, which is like a kingdom within England; it's a realm and Robin is its king. He sounds more and more as if he were a revolutionary: he has all the attributes of Castro in the mountains. All but one.

And here we come to what it is that Robin does not do. He does not Change the World. He has no plan, no program, no designs. He is not, as many scholars have maintained, a political holdout, the last of the Saxons fighting against their Norman conquerors. He has no lust for power. The wrongs he rights are personal and individual: it's *this* man who has been abused, not All Men. The same goes for his enemies. Every English county had its sheriff but the Sheriff of Northumberland was not in danger; just the one in Nottingham.

So what is Robin? He is the hero in a morality play. And the individuals and issues in that play were those known and felt by the people who invented him. Just as his character was a projection of the ideals of the peasantry, so were his deeds. He righted the wrongs they experienced, the abuses they lived with. And he did so in a way they believed was right and just.

Dating Robin is more controversial than it ought to be. The problem, of course, is that there were no written records. The ballads themselves are very little help here. The earliest of them were not recorded until late in the sixteenth century and a lot of changes can occur to an oral tradition in three to four hundred years. On top of which, the ballads, as we have them, are curiously devoid of references to historical events by which we could date them.

The first reference in print to Robin is found in *Piers Plowman* which, along with Chaucer's *Canterbury Tales*, is the most important work we have in Middle English. The work appeared, give or take, in the 1370s; by which time the legend of Robin was so widespread and had such currency that a passing reference was sufficient to identify him. Everyone knew who he was.

There are passages in the ballads which seem to make vague reference to events during the reign of Edward II. This would make Robin a fourteenth-century figure which, in view of the currency he had by 1370, is a solid hundred years too late. For an isolated peasantry with no freedom of movement to create a national hero, many decades have to pass.

Nor are all the references to Robin in Elizabethan literature much help here, though they do make clear that his legend was both known and loved throughout the kingdom—and by educated men and other classes than the peasantry. Robin appears in the writings of Shakespeare, Sir Philip Sydney, Ben Jonson, to name only the most famous. And his legend is included in Percy's *Reliques*, which, it's easy to forget, was used by Shakespeare as a source for many of his plays.

When was Robin, then? Clearly, he belongs to the 1200s; early, middle, take your choice. I have put him into King John's reign. Not just because I wanted to—I'd have done it, I suppose, in any case—but because I took it to be accurate. The special qualities of John's administration—the Interdict, the unique cruelties and corruptions, abuses so extreme that his own class turned against him—these are the right conditions to bring forth a Robin Hood.

There is a general concensus as to where it was that Robin lived: Lincolnshire, Yorkshire or Nottinghamshire. Each of these counties had large wooded areas; Robin's legend can't arise without a Royal Forest. More important is the density of place names in these shires. Even today, on local English maps, you will find them peppered with Robin Hood places: Robin Hood's Chase or Robin Hood's Bay or Robin Hood's Pricks—which, I've got to tell you, is a reference to archery.

Of the three counties, I can find no reason for not choosing Nottingham. It's true that Robin and his men did dress in "Lincoln green." In Robin's time, the city of Lincoln actually did produce a green dye for which it was famous. The dye, however, was in general use; like cambric which was made in Cambrai but available all over.

Aside from this, most of the place names—and there are surprisingly few of them—refer to Nottingham. We never read about the sheriffs in the other shires, and the forest, when it has a name, is Sherwood.

Enough about who Robin was and what and when and where. As to why, it is a question with a large variety of meanings. The one I have in mind, like Aristotle's final cause, addresses itself to purpose: what does the legend do, what is its function?

Why, in other words, does it exist? We've had a look at why it *did* exist; the pleasures it gave to a thirteenth-century peasantry, the needs and impulses it satisfied. But why should it survive for six hundred years? Why not some other story? With some other hero?

There must have been such stories. In 1960, thinking I'd write a play about Robin, I went to Sherwood Forest. There's almost nothing left of it; here and there some groves of trees between the housing developments. While I was there, I spent a night in Castleton, which is a small and ancient village in the Peaks district not far from Nottingham. And in the local pub, I had a conversation with a small and ancient farmer. And this farmer told me that never, ever in his life, had he been more than five miles from Castleton.

In Robin's time, the radius of a man's life was even smaller. The villages were all but sealed off from each other, few men traveled and few strangers came. Now, each of these clusters of people was subject to the same conditions, needs, abuses; to the same impulses to create heroes and legends. Which is what they must have done. There must have been God knows how many local myths. What happened to them all?

There are some heroes of the Middle Ages that we know about. We know them from the songs the troubadours and trouvères wrote and sang. Ballads about King Arthur and Richard the Lion-hearted and Charlemagne and Roland. And some others. These songs were written down; we have the texts. Roland has whatever life and currency he has because it's on the page and we can read the *Chanson*.

But Robin's legend is unique. Because—and this is central to the point I want to make—because it exists without its text. Who reads the Robin ballads? No one. Even scholars rarely bother to and there is not, so far as I know, a single modern academic book about them. Most of us don't even know the ballads are there at all. We're dealing with a poem few people know about and even fewer read. What makes it live? Where does its power come from?

I want to suggest that Robin lives for us for the same set of reasons that brought him to life in the first place. The peasants whose hero he was felt cheated, abused, angry, helpless, frightened, hopeless, vengeful or most of the above. It's a set of conditions which, in other times and other places, makes for revolution.

But not here. There was no agitation or revolt. Instead, there was a sublimation of these drives and feelings. If literally murdering your enemy is not, for whatever reasons, possible, you kill him in other ways. You mock him, you cut him down by ridicule. You isolate him from his source of power —the bishop is always alone in the woods—and discover he's no better or stronger than you are. You kill, in your fantasy, not the Great Power itself but some surrogate; the sheriff or his soldiers, not the King. The King is too important, too forbidden.

And the figure you choose to accomplish these things is like you, only more so; different in degree, not kind. So Robin was a peasant like the peasants who created him. He knew what they knew, did what they did, believed what they believed, endorsed their principles—all on a heroic scale; that is, the same but bigger.

Now, there being nothing truer than a true cliché, the more things change, the more they stay the same. And while our external conditions bear precious little similarity to those prevailing in thirteenth-century Nottingham, our internal conditions do. I have in mind, specifically, those conditions we experience while growing up.

The world we live in at the age of three or five or eight is one in which we often feel cheated, abused, angry, helpless, frightened, hopeless, vengeful or most of the above. While our enemies are sometimes the ratsy kid or the bully down the block, our most important enemies are those at home. Our family. We love them and we're loyal, like the peasant and his King. We hate them, too; our fantasies of Daddy being thrown out with the garbage. But we cannot kill them. Like the King, they're too important, too forbidden.

Robin acts on our behalf. We are the helpless ones that he protects. And his defense of us is always just and fair; he is no danger to our conscience. As we age, these feelings and these needs stay with us. Robin is not a child's hero and we're not reliving childhood when we love him as adults. As wise and as mature as we may grow, we still find satisfaction and release in Robin and his legend.

No laughter please, but I think Robin's myth is genuinely basic and important to us and its power comes from feelings that are downright primordial. I ask you, why should we love this archer when we've never drawn a bow? Why feel such pleasure when he makes a fool of someone mighty and then sets the bastard free? King John can't put me in a dungeon. He is not a danger to me—yet he is. The powers that he had, the passions he engendered, these things are alive in all of us. And Robin—honest, strong, resourceful, good, devout, a lover of his Maid and food and drink, susceptible to rage and vengeance, capable of fighting fair or foul with greater skill than any man but only when his cause is just—if he's not a catharsis and release for all these feelings that we can't act out, then seven hundred years of children and adults have made an inexplicable mistake.

So, Robin lives in your insides just as he does in mine. He is the hero you or I would be if we could be a hero.

Everything You Always Wanted to Know About Screenplays and Were Afraid to Ask

ny questions?"

I'm not a teacher, never taught a class; but every now and then, I'm asked to come and talk. I never lecture. Lecturing is work; you have to think and organize. So I walk in, sit down and, being nervous, light my cigar and smile out at the faces, hoping that they'll like me. Then, since the four jokes I remember never get a laugh, I'm apt to mutter, "OK, any questions? Ask me something."

Now, it happens that I've written plays and books for musicals and novels. On these subjects, there's a lot of interest, most of it intelligent. But when it comes to screenplays, what I get is: "How much do they pay you?" Or "What's Audrey Hepburn really like?" Then, after I've refused to answer, things get very quiet.

There's something very odd about screenplays. Something which arises from what most people think they are; which determines what, if anything, they want to know about them. Let me get at what I'm getting at by asking you a question: who writes screenplays? Name the names. Let's hear it for the author of *The Blue Angel* or *Casablanca* or *Mary Poppins*. I do this for a living and I couldn't tell you. But if I ask who wrote *Valley of the Dolls* or *Catch-22* or *The Gulag Archipelago*, the odds are you can tell me.

The screen writer is anonymous and why this is so is worth talking about. There are, it seems to me, two basic reasons why, one of them historical and the other dumb-headed.

Historically, movies don't seem to have had writers at all. I'm speaking, of course, of the silents. Someone, obviously, had to write the captions, just as someone has to pen the instructions that come with your dishwasher. But it's as difficult to give some writer praise or credit for *Intolerance* as it is to think of the creator of a Christmas pantomime as a playwright. Writing, we are prone to think, is words.

Not so. Aristotle, who is a permanent hero of mine, took the position that the elements of a play, in order of importance, were: plot, character, thought and then—and only then—diction. Now, movies are a branch of drama and a screenplay is a kind of play and on the screen you don't need words to tell a meaningful story about fully realized people. *City Lights* works without its captions. Though wordless, someone wrote it. But the point is, watching it, we feel that no one did. Movie writing came in through the back door. And it stayed there.

Why it stayed there also has to do with words. I've got to confess that I was in my early teens before it occurred to me that Someone actually wrote a movie. Tom Mix was a real man and he rode up on a real horse to a real corral. And when Tom spoke, it seemed like he was speaking for himself. Nobody wrote that "Howdy." He just up and said it.

If he sang it, we'd know different. For while singing is a natural thing, the invention of melody is not something most of us can do. But inventing sentences? We're all like Moliere's *Gentilhomme*: we've made the staggering discovery that everybody speaks in dialogue.

Or, put it this way. Improvising at the piano seems slightly miraculous. How does the fellow do it? But improvising dialogue occurs every time one opens one's trap. The inevitable result is that most of the conversation we hear in movies sounds to everyone, except the writer, as if nobody wrote it.

This misapprehension happens only rarely when

we see a play. For a lot of reasons, some of which are fairly interesting, we seldom think that an actor just happened to stroll in from the street to say whatever's on his mind. Someone put him there intentionally and wrote the words he's saying: which is the fundamental reason why playwrights get famous and screen writers don't.

We also know the words aren't improvised when the dialogue sounds, in one way or another, composed. I have in mind not only Bible epics—no one ever talked like that—but writing that is noticeably witty, stylish or complicated. *Notorious* seems "written," *Bullitt* does not: Steve McQueen seems to say whatever comes into his head, but Cary Grant is working from a script.

So by and large, the film writer is unknown because his work seems unwritten. This applies to writers great as well as writers small. If you look for the Faulkner of *As I Lay Dying* in his script for *The Big Sleep*, you'll have a hell of a time finding him. And this is not because he was writing down or for the money or because some vulgar studio head was eating him alive. A writer named Herman Mankiewicz wrote a script called *Citizen Kane* which I take to be as important a work as *A Farewell to Arms* and then some. But it did not make him a famous writer because, dumb-headed as it sounds, we're simply not aware of what he did.

And this, I think, is why the room goes still when I ask "Any questions?" They don't know what I do when I write a movie. How does a script come to be written, what does it contain, how does it get produced or cast?

I want to tell you the story of *Robin and Marian*. Not because it's typical or all that illuminating but because it happened to me and I like what I wrote and I'm proud of the film and the extraordinary actors who are in it.

Nothing, including having your show fold in Philadelphia, is more terrible for a writer than not writing. It has happened to me only once so far, this conviction that there's nothing in the world to write about, and the loss of identity you get is something close to terminal. It had been going on for months when I decided to take my best and only girl to the most expensive lunch then available in Manhattan.

We sat there not enjoying anything, not even my misery, when she asked me if, not having any new ideas, I had any old ones. "None," I said with that terrific certainty that comes from utter hopelessness, and then began to talk about this play I spent a year on and abandoned a decade ago. About the death of Robin Hood. I told the story, looked across the table at her. She was crying. So was I. And more or less together, what we said was, "It's a movie."

Bingo. There it was. Just take this old, unwritable idea and make a movie out of it. What happened next? In principle, I had two choices: I could go home and write it "on spec"—get it down on paper, then go look for a producer—or I could look for a producer first and get him to commission it.

Now, when I say I had a story, that's not altogether accurate. I had a fragment, bits and pieces. I knew how it started and I had an ending but the intervening ninety minutes were a blank. No producer in the world would buy it. On the other hand, I had running expenses that would make Atilla weep. So what I did was go to see my agent. I sat there in his office telling him my fragment, feeling more and more ridiculous, and when I stopped, Sam said—my agent's name is Sam: Sam Cohn.

Sam said, "Gee, Jim, that's terrific."

I said, "Really?"

"Absolutely."

"I'll be damned. I guess I'd better go home and write it."

"Don't do that," Sam said. "We'll sell it first."

I thought he was out of his mind. "You've got to be kidding."

But he wasn't—and we did. We went around from company to company, like a vaudeville team and I'd do my two-minute act, generally to polite applause. Then, one day, we played for the late Stanley Schneider of Columbia Pictures and—it still seems incredible to me—he commissioned it.

This is a highly unusual way for a film to begin. I didn't know what my story was or who most of the characters were or what the script would, in the end, be like. I even said so. Stanley didn't panic. My instructions were, in substance, to go off and do my thing. My script was free to take whatever form and shape it needed to. I felt like Haydn leaving the presence of Prince Esterhazy.

Some eight months later, I completed a first draft. Everyone concerned thought it was very good indeed. That was, roughly, in August 1971. Principal photography began in June 1975. What happened in between? Don't ask.

Which means I can't wait to tell you. First of all, what happened was Columbia Pictures fell upon hard times. They owned a film which they were willing to produce, but lacked the money to produce it. What happens with a motion-picture company in this condition is it sits. My script was bought and paid for and they might produce it someday. In the meantime, they had no objection to unloading it, the sole condition being that they get their money back.

I had two options. I could wait around or I could do what a producer does: I could package. To package this particular script, all I needed was two distinguished and important stars and/or a distinguished, important director. That's all. Except, of course, consecutively doesn't count; you have to have them all at the same time.

Ali, after the latest Frazer fight, described what this experience is like. Dying. I mean, you do not call David Lean on the phone and say, "Hi, Mr. Lean, sir. How about it?" You submit your script. You wait. The weeks go by. In Lean's case, months.

Then, finally, the answer filters back to you: no soap. On top of which, years later, an acquaintance of Lean's told me he never said no. He never said anything. The script never reached him, he never knew about it.

So it goes. At one time or another, most of the first-class leading men and directors you can think of read my script and said they'd like to do it. Or so it seems to me in retrospect. There were even times when we had all the pieces together simultaneously and crapped out.

Once, I've got to tell you this, we took our package to a major studio. The powers met. One of the powers—a businessman, hardheaded, practical—got up and told the story. By the end, his voice was choked and there were tears on both his cheeks. At which point, what he said was, "Gentlemen, I wouldn't touch this baby with a ten-foot pole. You might as well kill Tarzan." Which I thought then, and I still think, is a great idea.

How does a film get put together? In this case, by luck and accident. Which brings me to my Audrey Hepburn story. Several years ago, I attended the opening of one of Neil Simon's plays. The following day, a friend called up to say he'd been there, too, and wasn't she beautiful.

"Wasn't who beautiful?"

"Audrey Hepburn."

Now, I had, from the beginning, always dreamed of Miss Hepburn playing Maid Marian. It was as practical a dream as casting Carole Lombard. Miss Hepburn had retired. Her retirement was real. Not like Sinatra's: she was really not available.

Still, there she was. In town. At the Pierre. At this time, John Frankenheimer was to direct the film and he, too, was in town. I called him and told him my news.

"We'll send her the script," he said.

"We can't do that. It's rotten manners, she's here on vacation. It's an imposition and besides, she'll never read the thing and even if she does, she'll never play it."

"Right," John said, "on all counts—but we'll send it to her anyway."

So, the script was dumped, like an orphan, on her doorstep. The customary months went by. She'd never read it, obviously. Why should she bother to? Still, having utterly nothing to lose, John called her agent in Los Angeles and asked. The answer was: what script; she does not read scripts anymore. At this point, I'd have quit. John didn't. Would the agent be good enough to call the lady and ask? It's always seemed incredible to me, but apparently Miss Hepburn had been waiting patiently and quietly in Rome for someone to call her up and offer her the role. And for something like two years, she continued—patiently, quietly and with the most extraordinary loyalty and dedication—to wait while the production wobbled hopelessly from hand to hand on its ultimate way to Pamplona.

I've got a Sean Connery story, too. You have to understand that I'm sensational at casting; if there's a wrong actor for a role or a wrong role for an actor, I'll do it every time. I'm never right. So naturally, I thought Sean was born to play Little John. Sean definitely did not think so. I mean definitely.

Fade out. It's two years later and we have no leading man. By this time, I'd come to realize that Sean would make the finest Robin one could hope for. No point in hoping, though; he'd read the script, he'd turned one role down. With my knowledge of psychology, I knew that asking him was senseless. I said as much to Ray Stark, the producer. If only he had listened to me . . .

More stories. Richard Lester. It's 1973. Word reached me that Richard was much taken by the script and would like to direct it. At this time, one of the many productions that never happened was fully put together and the film already had a director. Still, I admired Richard's work and I was going to London for a vacation. Wouldn't it be nice to meet him? So I called.

Richard works at Twickenham Studios. Located in a section of London called St. Margaret's, which is a long way from anywhere, the studios look like a small abandoned lumberyard. Nothing much goes on there except Richard Lester films and lunch.

Lunch happens in a room designed along the lines of an East End workingman's café. Richard—who is generally a bit hysterical when he's working and a bit hysterical when he's not—was busy cutting a film. He came whizzing in and, for almost an hour, carried on about how smashing the script was. In detail and in general.

Basking in this, I mentioned a particular moment near the end. His face went blank. He frowned. Clearly, he'd forgotten this terrific whatever-it-was. I said so. He smiled.

"Forgotten it?" he said. "Not at all. I've never laid eyes on your script."

He never had. He'd heard about the story, found it fascinating and he'd gone around asking endless questions of anyone who'd read a copy. From then on, through all the muck, he hung on, stubbornly insisting that he must direct it. Two years after lunch was over, he was signed; the film was his.

Just one more casting story to illustrate how important planning and intelligence are. The role of King Richard was submitted to Nicol Williamson, and Richard Harris was asked to play Little John. They both said no. Consternation and confusion: what to do? They were asked to reconsider. Same result. Then, on the same day, six thousand miles apart and neither knowing about the other, they did the same thing: each asked for the other's role. So much for casting.

So there you are—your film's together. There's a director, a producer, the producer has the money, all the major roles are cast. What then? The script. What happens to the script is a mysterious sea change: the material, which was good enough to bring all these elements together, suddenly develops rickets, Parkinson's, a dose of acne and the croup.

As well it should. Nothing is ever good enough,

first drafts in particular. It's one thing to read a passage and imagine what it might be. And it's quite another to look with clear and steely eyes at what is there and think that Audrey Hepburn is going to have to stand up in front of most of the civilized world and say that line.

Ah . . . script discussions. In principle, they should be a duet between the writer and director. In practice, they're "The Hallelujah Chorus." The primary voices are The Studio, The Producer and The Stars. The Studio is financing and/or distributing the film; it markets the product. If it knows anything, it knows what sells. As luck would have it—and it's true of all the arts—nobody ever knows what's going to sell. Still, if you make your living doing a certain thing, it's only human nature to think you know what you're doing.

As a noun, "producer" is like "people": it looks singular but don't kid yourself. Producers generally rove in packs. Examine any large film ad. Above the title is a name—sometimes human, sometimes corporate—which "presents." And below the stars you'll find a list of titles: Executive Producer, just plain Producer, Associate Producer. All of them are concerned, and rightly so, about your script.

Then there are the stars. I'm terrified of setting foot onstage—I did it once in summer stock, three lines, and almost died of fright. I have a lot of compassion for stars; they're like the infantry, they've got to go out there and face it. In human terms, they have a right to criticize a script which I find deeper and more sympathetic than the studio's or the producer's.

As critics, though, stars often have two areas of weakness. They naturally tend to see a part of the film—their part—more clearly than the whole. And they also have a tendency to misconceive themselves. Just as I don't see my face as others see it. Or—think of the weddings you've attended and how clear your feelings sometimes are that the happy pair are wrong for each other. You see it but they don't. In much the same way, actors often don't know what they do best, what is right or wrong for them.

All these people can—and generally do—descend upon your script. With good intentions. No one wants to make a rotten film. And all these people should be listened to. Not merely because they are damn well entitled to be heard but because they are frequently right; and even when wrong, their mistakes can be illuminating.

The trouble comes—and I'm proud and happy to tell you that with *Robin and Marian* it never came—when things get out of balance. When the star absolutely insists or the producer absolutely demands or the studio fires off a fiat. This generally makes for chaos and catastrophe because making a film is really a lot like fighting a war: the director is the general and, until or unless relieved of his command, he must be rigorously obeyed. Not like some demented dictator; he listens to his chiefs of staff, considers their opinions, wavers or debates. But when he says "We march," you march.

Being a good director isn't easy. In addition to needing talent, experience and enormous physical and emotional strength, he has to wear two hats. During the planning of a film, he's the Supreme Commander, safe in his headquarters making big decisions. But once the shooting starts, he's out there with his troops, a Second Lieutenant facing the moment-to-moment risks and dangers.

So, Richard Lester, being a good director, listened to everyone while I sat and took notes. Then the two of us went off to his stark and somewhat creepy office at Twickenham and talked about the script.

What's actually in a movie script? The dialogue, of course. But what about the picture part of motion pictures? Who decides about what you see? And how and why?

I'm not much of an authority on film scripts. Most of the ones I've read are my own, which puts me in a terrific position to tell you what I do but not much else. Unlike a stage play—Shakespeare rarely writes more than "another part of the forest" or *"exeunt omnes"*—a substantial part of most filmplays consists of camera directions.

Of various kinds. Many scripts get very specific: "dolly," "pan," "track," "zoom" are words you see a lot. Or you will find detailed descriptions of the objects in a room or camera angles or what's in the foreground or what food is on the dinner table.

I don't do that. Ever? Only when the detail I specify is one that belongs to me. What I mean is, take the food on the table. If the character I'm writing is a glutton or a health nut, if he's ill or vain or takes no joy in life—in short, if it illuminates or brings alive or helps make real the figure that I'm writing, that's my territory. But if the food is not germane, if it doesn't tell you anything, then I don't care what's in the sandwich.

Or, take objects. If I'm writing the end of *Citizen Kane*, I'd better put a sled in that furnace with "Rosebud" painted on it. But other objects are in there burning, too. And they're burning in a particular furnace which has its particular age, size, shape, color. And it is situated in a furnace room which has specific characteristics. All these matters, God knows, are important. But they are for other hands, not mine.

I'm merely saying this: it takes a heap of hands to make a film. Every film has an art director, a set designer, a costume designer, a prop man—let alone a director. Each of these people is skilled or talented, or both, in what they do. And what they do, in principle, is to make concrete what the script implies.

Nor would I dream of telling a director where to put his camera. He knows, I don't. On top of which, it makes him angry. Now and then, of course, I do drop clues or make suggestions. These usually take the form of end results, of the effect that seems appropriate: "the room feels warm and cozy" or "light mist begins to rise" or "terror shows on Sandra's face." A good director knows these things, he doesn't need me to tell him. But many people depend on your script—from carpenters and makeup men to ad executives—and what you write must read for them as well.

A concrete example. Take the castle in the opening scene of *Robin and Marian*. The camera directions—that's me; my territory—say: "We see the castle; small, isolated, vulnerable, a fortress of no consequence." Those were the elements I thought germane to my story. The castle you see in the film is those things—and a whole lot more: it's strange, uneasy-making, bleak, a place where something terrible might happen.

All these things were implicit in the screenplay—something terrible does happen—and it's the director's sensitivities that make them explicit. He thinks about the scene, he feels it and in his imagination he "sees" something. He may not know exactly what he "sees" but he knows enough to tell what's wanted to his art director. The art director then either goes to picture books or takes his camera and goes himself to shoot some castles. Richard had perhaps a dozen castles on his desk to choose from. Making the right choice is instinctive: you just know it, that's your castle. You may then discover you can't shoot it because there's a power station or some damn thing fifty yards to the east of it, but that's part of the fun of picture making.

So Richard and I went over the script, agreeing for the most part on what was garbage and what wasn't. When we didn't agree, we'd discuss the point, more often than not coming up with a new solution that looked good to both of us. I then went home to New York, wrote for a month, went back to Richard whereupon we discovered that some of the old garbage had been replaced by new garbage. A few weeks of emergency repairs and that was that and I went home and stayed there. Until June in Pamplona.

Why Pamplona? Why shoot Sherwood Forest in the north of Spain? Well may you ask. Though it's easy for us to forget that not so many years ago, all the world was filmed in Burbank. Or that though the facade of the building you see Paul Newman walking into may be actually in Marrakesh, the bedroom scene that follows was probably shot in a studio thousands of miles away.

Still, why Pamplona? There are generally good reasons for location decisions of this kind. Money is a lot of them. The labor is cheap or there aren't any unions—which is why Yugoslavia—or your big star has a tax problem and can't set foot wherever. Or you've got to have ten thousand men in uniform and you can make a deal with Tito for a piece of his army. Or you need what looks like Russia and the closest you can get is Finland. Or the seasons are against you and you film the Andes in the Rockies; or the Andes are too far away and cost too much to get there. Endless reasons.

Some of these apply to *Robin and Marian*, but there were other factors. Take the weather. Almost every scene takes place outside and nothing, not one moment, calls for rain. There are passages you could film in a downpour if you absolutely had to, but the script is short on cover setups, places you can go when things get wet. And so much, on this point alone, for England.

Ireland? It's even soggier. Where, then? It turns out that there are parts, large parts of northern Spain which actually look like England. Honestly, no kidding. On top of which the weather in the summer is sensational, the labor costs aren't bad, Richard Lester had worked there several times before and liked it and we found a lot of castles and a Nottingham.

Pamplona was selected as the center of operations because it is a major city in the center of the various locations, and it has an air connection with Madrid where the photographic laboratories are. Of course, there was the Festival of San Fermin—the running of the bulls—which makes the city uninhabitable, and happened in the second week of shooting. Plus the character of Pamplona itself, which was such that almost everyone felt happier in hovels in the country.

Pamplona, if you haven't been there, looks like Bridgeport in the midst of a depression; dismal, grim and sour. The taste of the place is like last month's buttermilk. Even getting there is irritating. Either you drive north from Madrid on roads designed by Dracula or you fly in on Aviaco which, depending on your philosophy of life, is either hilarious or terrifying.

Have any of you ever seen a Fokker-27? You expect the Red Baron himself to be at the stick. Instead, it's a pleasant young Spaniard who comes out to tell you you can't leave Madrid for an hour or more because of the traffic. You look out the window. There isn't any traffic—there never is in Madrid. And so, you begin to wonder. When, a long time later, the motors rev and every soul in the cabin but you closes his eyes in prayer and crosses himself, you don't wonder anymore. You know.

Clearly, we took off and I got there. Along with —I don't know what to call her—my "friend and constant companion" who, by the time you read this, will be my wife. We go directly to the Tres Reyes, which is *the* hotel in town. It has all the disadvantages of the Holiday Inn in Providence which, believe me, is going some. It also has—or had that evening—Nicol Williamson in the lobby. He was, in the distinguished tradition of W.C. Fields, intently holding up a wall. I introduced myself. "Let's have a drink," he said.

I had the best time for the next few days. Other people were having problems—the imported manure for the streets of Nottingham was late in arriving; there wasn't enough water pressure to turn dry Spanish soil into English mud. Many such problems but none of them mine. No official script complaints and if people were changing my lines, they were craftily not telling me about it.

If you've never written a set, you can't imagine how it feels to see it actually standing there. It's so easy to sit at your desk and write "Three hundred wild stallions come charging over the hill." Or make it two hundred; what do you care as long as it's a lot of stallions. Well, somebody has to find those horses, rent them, transport them, watch them, feed them and get them to the set on time.

So, all I wrote was 'Cut to Nottingham.' I had to; either that or lose the big action sequence that happens there. Besides, what's a Robin Hood movie without Nottingham in it? And anyway, I wasn't asking for something outrageous like medieval London. Just a small, typical twelfth-century fortified town.

The art department built the damn thing. Actually, they found part of it—some outer ramparts, a church, some bits of wall, a few stone cottages; all thirteenth-century—and constructed the rest.

There were two ancient couples living in these cottages. They'd sit all day looking in blank disbelief at all these madmen making nonsense of the ruins in their front yard. In the end, rather than disturb them, we put costumes on them and they went on looking while we filmed. Any ancient faces you see peering out of windows while the Sheriff trots by really live there.

Fortified towns in Robin's time generally had the same basic structure. They were shaped roughly like a figure 8. The smaller circle of the 8—the inner bailey, just to show I know what it was

called—contained the quarters for the soldiers and the Sheriff, Lord or Earl, whoever held the local power. This was, of course, the heart of the fortification and it was here the townspeople would go in times of attack.

The townspeople lived in the bottom of the 8; plus possibly a scattering of cottages near the town walls. The life of the town—the shops, the marketplace—everything went on inside the walls. All this was built and filled with props and people. And all of it done as authentically as possible.

Most of what we know about the way things were and looked we know from pictures: tapestries, paintings and drawings and manuscript illuminations. Even what you see in the film that looks wrong is right. The cart bearing King Richard's casket is drawn by oxen not because the horses didn't show up that day but because, for some reason, oxen were used to move dead kings. At one point, the villain of the piece, Sir Ranulf de Pudsey, wields a mace and chain that looks like it came from F.A.O. Schwartz in a Camelot Kit. It didn't. Even things you don't see, such as what was worn as underclothing, are in period.

Some details weren't quite right; the people in the crowd, all locals, made their crowd noises in Spanish, and the takes began with the assistant director shouting *"Accion!"* But the manure was spread, the mud was rich, the flies were having a holiday and, looking at it all, it felt like stepping out of time and walking into Nottingham.

Since there was little for me to do in Pamplona except make people nervous and get in the way, we went to Madrid to watch the rushes. Each day's film was not only developed in Madrid, it stayed there. Because Richard Lester is, so far as I know, the only director on earth who doesn't look at rushes. This is not as lunatic as it sounds since Richard operates the principle camera—a practice forbidden in the States by union regulations—and is in a position to know what he's getting. I said principle camera just now because he usually has several going at once, a technique which saves time and money and drives his actors crazy. They never know which way to look or if they're on camera or not. It also tends to raise the interior intensity of performance. It's a bit like being surrounded by an invisible enemy; you have to be vividly alert and alive all the time.

Rushes. The English call them dailies which is much more accurate, especially in Spain where no one hurries very much. Monday's rushes consist of only those takes filmed on, let's say, Friday after which the director said, "Print it." A lot of takes are never printed. An actor blows a line, a horse refuses to behave, the crowd moves left instead of right and blocks the shot, some kid who's watching the action decides to bolt through the background; any number of reasons.

The amount of film printed each day varies enormously. To begin with, you have to set things up before you can shoot something. Some setups are easy and quick; a single actor dozing on meadow grass in sunshine, for example. But shooting a battle scene at night can take you hours to prepare. Then, some directors are fast and some slow. David Lean, with *Ryan's Daughter*, waited months for just the right storm to happen and, when it didn't, moved from one continent to another to get it. Richard, on the other hand, will shoot almost no matter what.

When the *Robin and Marian* dailies were printed, they went to the film editor; or cutter, as the English, again more accurately, call him. What he does is cut and splice, selecting those takes which he thinks are best and assembling them into story sequence. The cutter's function can range from that of a mere technician to being an important creative contributor to the quality of a film.

The cutter works in a studio which, for his purposes, can be anything from a small hotel room with a Movieola in it on up. In Madrid, things were distinctly up; a modern building full of cutting and projection rooms. The movie business is stone-cold dead in Spain and, making little of their own, they do a lot of dubbing into Spanish, which is what went on there. Except for us.

So every day we had from ten to twenty minutes' worth of entertainment. Watching—or "reading"—rushes is a fascinating business. It is also highly tricky and deceptive. What you see, each take, is like a single stone in a mosaic. The stone itself may be beautiful or flawless but you cannot tell how it will fit into the whole; or even if it fits at all.

The takes we saw were wonderful. Clean, full of feeling, artless, artful, real and beautiful to look at. And the pieces fit; the stones all go together and the picture that they make is glorious. Of course, that's just the writer speaking. It's a rare thing for a writer when his work turns out the way he hoped it would. Some things are always wrong or disappointing and they're usually vital things. Perfection, everybody knows, is unattainable; but this film comes close. That's not a judgment of my work; my writing's always full of flaws. A film can only be as good as its ingredients but given what I wrote—the characters, the story that they tell—the end result is everything I ever dreamed. And more. Whether or not it's actually this good, well that's a judgment you must make.

And so much for writing screenplays. Reading screenplays, which is what I hope you are about to do, can be a problem. Most of us, I think, are put off by a page of script because of Shakespeare. High-school Shakespeare, wading through *Macbeth*, not knowing half the words and even if you looked them up it didn't help because the syntax was all screwed around; and all those semicolons.

In point of fact, scripts are difficult to read and an amazing number of people who do it for a living at studios don't know how to read them. The basic reason for this is that the script is not written to be read in the first place. It is written to be seen.

By dumb luck, however, I think I have devised a way for screenplays to be read. In the text that follows, every line of dialogue is there intact. Between the lines, however, you will find no camera directions; not one "Cut to." In their place is prose that helps to tell the story. It's a cross between a novel and a screenplay and I think it works like Gangbusters—and anyway, the text is full of pictures.

"Any questions?"

I

No More Crusades

The Great Crusade was over. Armies of a size no living man had ever seen had been assembled. Kings from England, Germany and France, each followed by his Bishops, Earls and Counts and Knights and slaves and peasants set out, marching to Jerusalem. They never got there.

They came close. There was a day when they could see the Holy City dimly in the distance, far across the desert plain. They paid a high price for the view: the death of tens and tens of thousands. Battle deaths and deaths from plague and shipwreck, drought and famine. During the Seige of Acre, England's Richard Lionheart himself came close to death from fever.

Richard was a legend in his own time. All of Europe knew the story of his life, the poets and the mistrels wrote and sang about him. No King since Charlemagne had been so celebrated. He was sensitive and highly cultured, he wrote poetry and music, he was trained in Latin, Greek and other languages. He was a brilliant military man: strong, fearless, wise, a great tactician and a natural leader. He was also brutal, cruel and sadistic. He loved war.

He found enough of it. England's territory, in those days, included half of France. The western half, from Normandy along the Channel Coast to Aquitaine, which touched the Spanish border. Eight provinces in all. Each province had its counties, every county had its count and they were endlessly at war. With one another or with Richard. Local wars; not battles for the history books, but a revolt is a revolt and Richard's kingdom, held in one by little threads, required constant mending.

So, if you had been near Chaluz Castle on an early April morning in 1199, you would have known what you were looking at.

Chaluz was not important. Neither large nor rich nor advantageous militarily, it stood, and still stands, in southwestern France, about a hundred miles inland from the ocean coast. Chaluz Castle, whose function it was to defend and protect the town, was for some strange reason nowhere near it.

Instead, it stood several miles away, isolated and vulnerable on open farmland. Like the town, it was a place of no importance. Nothing memorable was meant to happen there.

The sky, on this particular morning, was overcast and the fields, untouched by Spring, looked dank and gray. No sheep, no shepherds; nothing moved except a line of men, trudging slowly toward the castle.

The men were soldiers. On their worn and muddy uniforms were English emblems. Richard's men. Crossbowmen, foot soldiers—less then fifty in all—and two Officers on horse. A number of the men on foot were pushing, pulling at a piece of siege machinery, grunting it across the muddy field.

When the machine, a mangonel, was within firing range—a hundred yards or so from the castle walls—the soldiers stopped. Large rocks were found and one was fastened to the mangonel. The crossbowmen deployed themselves. The siege was ready to begin.

The officer in charge, a Captain, was a big man: gray and grizzled, bearded, powerful and weather-

beaten, close to fifty. The other man on horse was very like him, only gentler looking and, if anything, more powerful. Their names were Robin Hood and Little John.

They were looking at the castle, frowning. It seemed curiously silent, still. No archers on the

battlements, no men in armor; nothing. Robin turned and signaled toward the mangonel.

Its long arm was released, hurling the great stone at the end of it into the air. It arched against the sky and crashed against the castle wall—and still no movement from within, no answering fire.

Robin turned to Little John.

ROBIN: See anything?

John shook his head.

JOHN: You think it's deserted?

ROBIN: Why not? It's a damn fool's errand we're on in the first place.

Robin turned and signaled to his crossbowmen. They raised their weapons, fired, and the arrows flew, striking the battlements and skittering across the stones. Still, silence from the castle; no response. John turned to Robin.

JOHN: If they've gone off with the treasure, Richard isn't going to like it.

ROBIN: If there ever was a treasure. One more flight.

Their eyes stayed on the castle as the bowmen fired again. Then, amusement and surprise lit both their faces.

ROBIN: By God, John—

JOHN: Will you look?

High atop the castle wall, a single man was standing. Ancient—he was tall and gaunt and over sixty, with long white hair and beard. In one hand, he was holding an enormous frying pan and, as the arrows rained down on his head, he used it as a shield to ward them off.

Robin and John took one look at each other, grinned, dug in their heels and went cantering up to the castle. Above them, the old man was busy picking up the arrows that had landed near him. Robin and John reined in, looked up. The old man looked down. Robin, trying to be serious about it, said:

ROBIN: I speak for Richard Lionheart, King of England, Lord of half of France and thereby Overlord of this domain.

OLD MAN: I'm up here speaking for myself.

ROBIN: Where are your soldiers?

OLD MAN: Run off.

ROBIN: And the Lord of Chaluz, where is he?

OLD MAN: He led 'em.

JOHN: Ask him if he knows about the treasure.

OLD MAN: Left me here with all the women and the children and no weapons anyplace. God's blood, there's not a tooth left in my head and here I am collecting arrows and you think I've got a bow to shoot them with?

ROBIN: My King believes your Lord is keeping treasure from him and my orders are to get it.

OLD MAN: That would be the treasure people say was found by Jean the Ploughman. Great gold statue three feet long, they tell you.

ROBIN: That's the one.

OLD MAN: Well, I was with him when he found the thing and what he dug up was a rock.

ROBIN: We're fighting for a rock.

OLD MAN: You want to look, it's out there in the turnip field—we couldn't lift it so we left it lay—and what I've come to say is if there's got to be a fight, I'm all there is and you can come and get me.

ROBIN: You're a mad old man.

Robin grinned up at the old man, tossed him a salute and, turning, looked around.

JOHN: What now?

ROBIN: I want to give that rock to Richard.
           Where's the turnip patch?

They started off, then stopped. What stopped
them was the view across the fields. In the near
distance, riding furiously toward them, were two
horsemen. And, behind them, clattering and trying
to keep up, twenty or more knights in full armor.

Richard Coeur de Lion rode one horse and Mercadier the other. Richard was a man of forty-four
who looked like what he was: a hero gone wrong.

Still vigorous and powerful, he had become a
feverish and driven man, decayed and dangerous.
Mercadier was famous as a soldier, too, in those
days. A professional, a mercenary, he was Richard's
favorite commander.

The two men raced up and reined in by John
and Robin. Richard, who was known and feared
for fits of rage, looked taut and angry. He was
breathless but his voice had snap and bite and what
he said to Robin was:

RICHARD: What kind of siege is this? Where is the Lord of Chaluz? Where's my treasure?

ROBIN: Gone.

RICHARD: My treasure's gone?

ROBIN: The Lord is gone. The treasure never was.

RICHARD: A golden statue three feet long: I want it.

Robin looked straight at his King. His face was set. He shook his head and turned to go when Richard shouted:

RICHARD: Captain!

ROBIN: Yes, my Lord?

RICHARD: I ordered you to take this castle.

ROBIN: Yes, my Lord?

RICHARD: Well, take it. Bring it down and get my statue.

ROBIN: They surrender, and your statue is a stone.

RICHARD: I want it done.

ROBIN: There is no treasure.

RICHARD: Do it.

ROBIN: Kill them all? There's not a soldier in the place; just children and a mad old man.

RICHARD: What's that to me?

ROBIN: It should mean something.

RICHARD: Is that disapproval, Robin? Am I in the wrong?

ROBIN: I've followed you for twenty years. I fought for you on the Crusade, I've fought for you in France. Show me a soldier and I'll fight him for you now. But I won't slaughter children for a piece of gold that never was.

RICHARD: I order it.

Robin turned to look at John. They'd been through everything together, thirty years and more of it. Richard's voice rose.

RICHARD: I command you!

ROBIN: No; you do it. You're a bloody bastard, you'll enjoy it.

RICHARD: Damned right I'll do it. Mercadier! Arrest them. Lock them up. I'll have their heads on pikes.

Livid with rage, Richard whirled on the knights behind him, roaring:

RICHARD: I want these walls down! Every damned head in this place!

His back was to the castle as the old man on the battlements above him shouted:

OLD MAN: Lionheart!

He was standing there, the old man was, eyes wild, at his full height, a picture of demented majesty. One hand was raised above his head. It held an arrow.

OLD MAN: Lionheart, you are a pig!

With which, he hurled the arrow with tremendous force. Richard, blind with anger, spun back toward the castle. As he moved, the arrow struck him in the shoulder near his neck. It went deep. He sat absolutely still. Then, as if nothing had happened, his hand steady, under complete control, he reached up to remove the arrow.

It was stuck, embedded in his flesh. He pulled at it and pulled again. Then, with a roar of rage, he snapped it off. The broken shaft protruded from his shoulder. Richard didn't seem to feel it. Shouting orders to his knights, he took position on the field.

He led the charge, as savagely as if there had been soldiers in the castle. Robin and John, with Mercadier to guard them, sat and watched it all. The great rocks arching from the mangonel, the flights of arrows, knights at gallop, broadswords. And sounds: the horses and the clank of armor, crashing walls, the cries and screams. And at the end, of course, the smoke and flames as what was burnable was burned.

Smoke still drifted from the castle as the evening mist began to rise. Richard, thoughtful and alone, was standing in the turnip field. His eyes looked at the ground before him, at a large, half-covered stone. He didn't seem to hear as Mercadier came toward him through the mist, a ragged-looking man one step behind him. The man carried a shabby leather bag. He went to one knee near his King and opened it: there were surgeon's tools inside.

Richard turned. His voice was brisk and wry and
what he said was:

RICHARD: Well . . . perhaps it was a stone. Is this
a barber surgeon?

MERCADIER: Yes, my Lord.

SURGEON: I travel with your men, sire; I look
after them.

RICHARD: With much success?

He started taking off his tunic as he said to Mercadier:

RICHARD: You've seen to John and Robin?

MERCADIER: Under guard. They're on their way to Chaluz.

RICHARD: Good.

Naked to the waist, he sat down on the ground. The surgeon stood there, terrified to put a knife into his King.

RICHARD: Come on, come on. The patient's cold; the doctor sweats.

Reluctantly, the surgeon came.

SURGEON: The arrow will be hard to reach.

RICHARD: That makes it all the more worthwhile. Don't be afraid; I generally enjoy the pain.

The surgeon nodded and began to work. Richard, as if nothing in the world was going on, said thoughtfully:

RICHARD: You heard it, Mercadier. I told him to attack: he told me no. I ought to kill him for it.

MERCADIER: Will you?

RICHARD: I don't know; I'm a moody fellow, it depends upon the mood. I killed them all this afternoon. Except the old man; let him go, I liked his eyes. But Robin? We've been friends, you see, for twenty years. I was in Nottingham, near Sherwood, when we met. He was a local hero. Robbed the rich, they said. I needed men for the Crusade. He was the best that ever came to me.

He looked up at the surgeon and his voice was sharp.

RICHARD: Get on with it. I'll die of old age at this rate.

This said, he turned to Mercadier again.

RICHARD: So, off we went to do great things. We led three hundred thousand soldiers to the Holy Land and came back on a ship with fifty. Not at all what we intended. Christ, I do what must be done, I have no choice, but Robin judges me. That's what he does. The peasant bastard. Judge a King?

Rage rising, he shoved the surgeon aside.

RICHARD: You butcher! Watch—I'll show you.

Richard got up to his feet. He seized the broken arrow shaft with both hands, pulled with all his strength. The shaft came free. He thrust it toward the surgeon.

RICHARD: King's blood. Remember it. I should've killed the old man, too.

He hurled the arrow down and ground it with his heel. Then, anger spent, he shivered. Mercadier picked up his tunic, gently draped it over him.

RICHARD: It's cold. I never liked the dark. How long is it to Chaluz? Half an hour?

Mercadier nodded. Side by side, they started walking slowly through the mist. He was a bit unsteady, Richard was, and Mercadier moved to him, took his arm.

RICHARD: A little rest . . . and then I'll tend to Robin and John. Mercadier, you stay with me tonight. I want to drink before I sleep.

II

The Death Watch

It was dark and little could be seen of Chaluz. On a street no wider than an oxcart, men were moving. Heavy footsteps on the ground, then silence, then the clank of iron bolts, the opening of a massive door.

There was a slit of light, and into it stepped Robin, striding through the doorway. After him came John. And then an officer. The room they entered, down a flight of worn stone steps, was narrow, lit by torches mounted on its thick stone walls. Around the room were casks of wine and empty bottles.

Robin and John stood there, calm and impassive, while the officer took in the cellar, nodded briskly, satisfied, turned sharply and went up the steps and out the door. They watched in silence, John and Robin did, until the bolts went thudding into place. Then, turning on each other, they exploded.

JOHN: Sweet Jesus, Robin.

ROBIN: What would you have done? You tell me? Kill the old man, kill the women, kill the children? What?

JOHN: You didn't save them, did you? They're all dead and we're in here.

ROBIN: I didn't make you come along.

JOHN: You looked at me.

ROBIN: You nodded.

JOHN: What would you have done?

ROBIN: I know, I know.

He took a deep breath and he looked around the cellar.

ROBIN: Ah, John, what did I get us into? I could have talked to Richard, could have tried. I didn't have to call him names.

JOHN: He is a bloody bastard.

ROBIN: Are we any better? Don't we serve him?

JOHN: He's our King.

ROBIN: I took him for a great King. There we were in Sherwood, robbing abbots, giving pennies to the poor. It didn't seem like much compared to rescuing the Holy Land. I wonder sometimes if we ever should have left.

John shrugged and brought out a chunk of bread from somewhere in the folds of his tunic.

ROBIN: How can you eat?

JOHN: I'm hungry.

ROBIN: Look at you, you've got a belly, old and gray. They reckon forty as a good life and we're past it.

JOHN: My poor Dad and all the Dads before him lived in Barnesdale. One small town, that's all they ever knew. I've known a King, I've been across the world, I've seen Jerusalem—the sand was blowing and .the walls were miles away but— I'd have thought I've had a good life. As for Richard, you don't think he means to kill us?

ROBIN: I don't know him anymore, I do not know the man.

JOHN: He cares too much for you.

ROBIN: I cared for him: these things can stop.

JOHN: Well, if we go, at least we'll go together.

ROBIN: Is that your idea of dying?

JOHN: I've got no idea of it at all. You'd think I'd learn; I've seen enough of it.

ROBIN: I'll tell you this much: I'm not dying quietly.

The two men looked at one another and, as Robin took John's bread and tore off a piece of it, they grinned. And then—no need to speak; they knew each other much too well for that—they looked around the room.

The walls were far too thick. The door, the only door, had bolts and guards outside. The ceiling? It was ten feet high and vaulted. In it—as there always was in rooms that had no chimneys—was a slit. An opening between the stones.

One quick nod. Then Robin reached down for an empty bottle. Then he broke it. John was ready, in a half-crouch underneath the slit. Robin, a gleaming, pointed shard of glass in hand, was on John's shoulders in one bound. John straightened. Robin reached up. With the glass, he started scraping at the mortar in between the massive stones. Glass on mortar; it might take forever and they knew it. Still, as Robin scraped away, John looked at him and grinned.

JOHN: If I'd not met you, think what I'd have missed.

III

It nearly worked. Countless hours, broken bottles. Dawn had come and no one came to kill them. They had lost all track of time and Robin's hands were bleeding when, at last, the large stone by the ceiling slit came free. They stood there, braced to bear the weight of it, as the bolts were pulled back on the cellar door.

Mercadier stood in the doorway. His eyes were red from lack of sleep, his face was drawn and gray. His voice was flat, no feeling or expression, as he said:

MERCADIER: The King will see you now.

He turned and went. They followed. Up the steps and out into the sunlight, down the narrow street, across a tiny square to where the Great Hall stood.

The Hall was full of people, knights and noblemen and women, all in court clothes, celebrating something. In a corner, court musicians played gay music. Couples danced, dogs prowled and servants rushed about with food and wine.

Mercadier led John and Robin through the press of people. There was smoke—a fire blazing in the center of the floor—and it was hard to see. Ahead, the crowd was thicker. They pushed through and there was Richard, dancing with a lady of the court.

The King was barely recognizable. His flesh was gray, cold sweat poured down his face. His eyes were bright with fever and his neck was wound around with bandages.

Richard, in high spirits, grinned at Robin when he saw him, and his voice was coarse but strong.

RICHARD: We are celebrating our demise. I'd always fancied leaving from a larger stage but my physician—funny fellow, my physician. I've already had him hanged: it seemed a fair exchange.

He shouted at a servant passing by.

RICHARD: Wine! Bring a bucket of it.

Then, turning back to Robin and John:

RICHARD: You—you're not for hanging. You're for cutting up and I'd have done it if it hadn't been for this.

ROBIN: Will that be all, my Lord?

RICHARD: All? Damn your all; all done, all over. Father cursed me when he died. I killed him and he felt resentful. He'd have loved this.

He broke off as the servant returned with a tankard of wine.

RICHARD: I said a bucket!

The servant rushed away and Richard's eyes went back to Robin.

RICHARD: John's the next King. You remember John. John Lackland he was called, but he gets all the lands now. Christ, why did I have no children? Never gave a damn for England; never there. Not even as a corpse. They're planting me in France: by Father. You're not dancing. Want a girl? A boy? Have Mercadier; he likes it. Did I ask for wine? Take something from me.

ROBIN: Nothing, sire.

RICHARD: He pouts, he sulks; he gave his life to Richard and he's sorry. You don't know what sorry is. I was a King. My mother —she'll be eighty soon, the bitch. I've sent for her. You think she'll come?

The servant returned with a bucket of wine and Richard grabbed it from him as he said:

RICHARD: Clever fellow, Death is. Wouldn't take me on my terms. God knows I tried to find him. Ask for something, damn you.

Not waiting for an answer, Richard raised the bucket, drinking greedily, spilling the wine all over himself. Robin's answer, when it came, made Richard taut with rage.

ROBIN: It's too late, there's nothing left.

RICHARD: There's still your life. You take me for an equal. Always did. I'll carve you yet, you peasant bastard. Mercadier! My sword! While I am King—

His words were choked off as his body twisted in a sudden spasm of pain.

ROBIN: Richard!

The music stopped. The Hall was very still. Richard seemed about to fall as Robin put his arms around him and the two men went down slowly to the floor.

ROBIN: Richard, it's me.

RICHARD: I know it's you. You couldn't leave me, could you.

Robin shook his head.

RICHARD: You're free of me. I let you go.

Then, making what he meant to be a smile, Richard said:

RICHARD: What will you do now, Jolly Robin, now I'm dead?

IV

Everything looked gray. Light rain was falling softly down. On Mercadier and on the line of knights that followed him along the narrow, rocky road. On Richard's casket, lying on a crude, black, open wagon, on the dozen oxen pulling it.

And on Robin and on John. The two men knelt there in the mud along the roadside, watching as their King was drawn away. And even after the procession passed, they went on kneeling.

Robin was the first to rise. Then John. They looked at one another.

JOHN: It's all over, isn't it?

Slowly, Robin nodded.

JOHN: What now?

ROBIN: We watched him die, he saw us there. He won't mind if we miss the funeral.

Robin turned, went to his horse and mounted. John, as always, followed him.

JOHN: Where do we go? Which way?

ROBIN: West.

JOHN: Why west?

ROBIN: England's there. Come on, John, let's go home.

JOHN: To Sherwood, Robin? Back to Sherwood?

Robin nodded and John's eyes filled up with tears. He smiled through them.

It seemed to take no time at all. It did, of course; it took them months to make the journey. But it seemed as if the gray of France was suddenly the green of England. Sun and shade and rolling meadowland.

They cantered through the English green. Past tiny towns and open fields; a little farmhouse here or there, a flock of sheep untended on a hillside. Splashing through streams, by merchants trudging on the roads and men on pilgrimage.

The day came when they knew exactly where they were. The sun was high, the sweat ran down their grimy faces as they galloped on an ancient Roman road up to a hilltop.

At the crest, they reined in and looked out across the valley. Farmland for a mile or so and then a forest rose, as dense and thick as if it were a fortress wall. It stretched on, untouched, absolutely wild, as far as they could see.

Both of them were smiling, breathless from the ride.

JOHN: There she is.

ROBIN: I'll race you.

Both of them let out a roar, dug in their heels, went plunging down the hillside and across the fields. To Sherwood Forest.

The woods were actually like a wall and, as they raced along the edge, they almost missed the path. They turned, at full speed, and went plunging in. They knew this forest, every twist and turn and stone and tree.

At least, they'd known it once. But as the day stretched on and as the path grew narrow, and forked and forked again, they both began to wonder. It was twilight when Robin, moving very slowly, turned his mount away from the path and started through the undergrowth.

ROBIN: You sure?

JOHN: I'm sure.

John shrugged and followed. Twenty yards or so they went; and then, the growth too dense to move through, they drew up. It struck John funny.

JOHN: A lot of grass can grow in twenty years.

ROBIN: I know these woods.

JOHN: Good place to pass the night.

ROBIN: We're going through—

There were sudden crashing sounds and both men stiffened, reaching for their swords.

ROBIN: What's that?

The sounds receded and, with sheepish grins, they both said:

JOHN & ROBIN: Deer . . .

Robin shook his head, dismounted, drew his sword and started hacking at the undergrowth. It was hard work and slow. But suddenly, there was no more of it and Robin, breathless, stumbled through into a clearing.

ROBIN: John . . .

John was just a step behind. They stood there,
looking at what used to be their camp. A little
valley, cut through by a stream; high trees on all
sides, weeds and grass waist-high. A single oak
tree—Robin's Oak—stood in the open.

They started running to the tree. Around them,
fallen down, decayed and rotten, were the rem-
nants of their camp: the crumbled foundations of
huts, open storage pits filled with debris and thick
with moss, a cooking hearth, all overgrown. They
pulled up, winded, near the Oak.

JOHN: There's nothing left.

ROBIN: What did you think there'd be?

JOHN: I didn't think . . . I never thought . . .

John turned and wandered off as Robin, looking
at his Great Oak said:

ROBIN: I wonder if it's there.

He reached up, stretching to a large, low branch.
His fingers, remembering the way, inched on and
found a hollow. In it, where he'd left it all those
years ago, was his hunting horn.

He brought it out, a ram's horn, heavily en-
crusted with moss and mould. He tapped it; muck
fell out. Then, smiling at himself, he raised it to
his lips to blow. He stood there very still, remembering.

He never blew the horn. Instead, there was a
sudden whizzing sound. An arrow quivered in the
great oak, inches from his head.

V

The Old Boys

It all happened very quickly. Robin spun around and saw a hooded figure moving toward him through the underbrush, fitting another arrow to his bow. And just behind him came a second hooded man who held a massive quarterstaff.

John raced to Robin's side. No time to draw their weapons. They crouched, then bounded toward the hooded figures. For a moment, all of them were tangled up. Then Robin was astride one man and John the other.

John looked down. The man beneath him was an old man. Gray and gaunt and sixty.

JOHN: Christ, Robin, it's an old man.

ROBIN: So's mine.

Robin's man looked up at him. A heavy man, a ruddy, grizzled face. There was wonder on the face; and disbelief.

HEAVY MAN: Robin? It's us, it's Tuck and Will.

ROBIN: Is that you, Tuck?

FRIAR TUCK: Oh Jesus, Robin, you've come home.

He sat up, Tuck did, eyes on Robin, threw his arms around him and burst into tears.

There was a lot of hugging after that, a lot of talk. And drinking, too. Will Scarlet built a fire, Tuck produced some venison and all four sat around the fire in the darkness telling stories, feeling young.

Then Will picked up his lute and, in a soft sweet voice, began to sing. It was a long song and the end of it went:

WILL: Follow him, follow him, bloody and brave;
I'll follow bold Robin from here to the grave.

The Baron of Bedford, he slew with one stroke;
The Duke of Doncaster, he hung from an oak.
And evil Prince John took one look at his sword
And fled to his castle and prayed to the Lord.

The Sheriff had five hundred men on the field;
But Robin and John, not an inch did they yield.
The green of the meadow turned slowly to red:
Of the five hundred men, there were five hundred dead.

Brown ale and good meat, Robin has it to spare,
And he'll give you to eat if your larder is bare.
And if you've a taste for the song that I sing,
Come join me in Sherwood where Robin is king.

Follow him, follow him, bloody and brave;
I'll follow bold Robin from here to the grave.

Robin, more pleased than he cared to admit, looked at John with wry amusement.

ROBIN: They've turned us into heroes, Johnny.

Then, he looked at Will and, just a bit suspicious, said:

ROBIN: Will, you didn't make it up?

WILL: These songs, I don't know where they come from but you hear them every-place. We go from town to town—

TUCK: He sings, I cut a purse or two.

WILL: And everywhere we go, they want to
          hear about the things you did.

ROBIN: But Will, we never did them.

WILL: I know that. And then again, some days
          I'm not so sure.

John picked a stick up, stirred the coals.

JOHN: I think I'll go by Barnesdale in the
          morning, see my Dad.

TUCK: He died, John; years ago.

John put the stick down, smiling sadly at the
coals.

JOHN: He'd not have known me anyway.

ROBIN: What happened here when we went off?
          Did Marian—is she alive?

WILL: Last time we passed through Notting-
          ham. She lives down Kirkly way, not
          far.

ROBIN: How is she? Is she well?

Will nodded.

ROBIN: And happy, too?

Will nodded once again.

ROBIN: That's good, that's very good. I told
          her she'd be happier without me. Lovely
          girl; I haven't thought of her in years.
          What happened to the Sheriff?

WILL: He still rules the county, he's more
          powerful than ever.

ROBIN: Those were good days, fighting him.
          I've never had a better enemy. What
          about the others, all the rest of us?

TUCK: They died or went away; not all at
          once but through the years. Just Will

and me; we stayed. Once the Crusades were over, we were sure you'd come again. You didn't, so we took you to be dead and off we went.

ROBIN: How is it in the towns around now? Still as bad?

WILL: We've never known such times. King John, he must be mad. The looting and the killing; his own kind have turned against him and the kingdom falls apart. He's married to a child, the Queen is twelve years old, and all he does, they say, is stay in bed with her.

TUCK: And, did you know, he's fighting with the Pope. John's soldiers pillage all our churches and you can't hear Mass or take Communion anywhere in England.

WILL: If there ever was a time for us, it's now. We travel through the towns, we watch and listen and they'd come to you, the people would. They'd come to Robin if he called.

TUCK: And by the hundreds; like the old days, only greater, and the things we did before would seem like nothing.

ROBIN: So we fight against the King?

He smiled, Robin did—the idea was ridiculous —and shook his head.

ROBIN: Sing us another song, Will. One that really happened.

WILL: Why'd you come back, Robin?

ROBIN: Not to fight.

He leaned back, looking at the fire.

ROBIN: Maid Marian? Is there a song about her? Does she have one?

Will picked up his lute again.

WILL: Come, sweet Maid,
      Come live with me;
      Be not afraid,
      For what will be
      Will be. Ah Marian, what do we care
      For all the griefs and wars out there?

Will's voice, the song unfinished, hung on a
high, soft note as John said, almost dreamily:

JOHN: Still, it would be something, Robin,
         wouldn't it?

ROBIN: To do it one more time?

John nodded. Robin didn't move at all. He merely
looked into the fire.

ROBIN: One more time . . .

WILL: Live with me in my forest glade.
      Come Marian, come my sweet Maid.

They ate, they talked—about the old days mostly
—and eventually they slept.

VI

Reunions

They were up before the sun, all four of them, and they had left the forest and were out in open farmland by the time the church bells rang the first hour of the day.

They were moving east, toward Nottingham, when Robin stopped and listened. Faintly, he could hear a bell. The sound came drifting from the west, from Kirklytown. Robin paused, then turned and started toward the sound.

JOHN: Aren't we going to Nottingham?

Robin shrugged, as if it couldn't matter less.

ROBIN: I think we'll go by Kirkly first.

As they turned and rode off slowly through the morning mist, the bells in Nottingham were ringing, too. Slow, heavy claps of sound from the great church there. The church was very old and vast; it loomed up over everything.

There was little movement in the outer courtyard where the townsfolk lived, their tiny houses lining narrow streets, the whole of it encircled by a fortress wall. But in the inner courtyard, where the Sheriff and his soldiers lived, the day was underway.

Out in the muddy yard were soldiers drilling. Several of them, heavy battle swords in hand, were practicing the moves of combat, clanging sword sounds mixing with the bells.

The Sheriff did not hear the noise. He stood inside his study in the castle tower reading from a Latin text. He was a remarkable man, the Sheriff. In a time when noblemen took illiteracy as a mark of distinction, he had taught himself many languages, and the room was full of heavy tomes and scientific instruments and paintings. He stood there —vigorous and powerful at forty-five—and looked up from the beautifully illuminated page, all decorated with dragons, gargoyles, dreadful beasts. He smiled.

THE SHERIFF: The monsters always come out better than the saints.

He heard the clatter from the courtyard then, looked out the window, shook his head.

THE SHERIFF: They never learn.

Moments later, he was out there in the yard, his battle sword in hand. The men who had been drilling looked at him apprehensively as he barked out:

THE SHERIFF: First two men: both at once. The rest of you clods, pay attention.

The two soldiers hesitated, then lumbered forward. The Sheriff's moves were almost too fast to follow as he swung, dodged and swung again. Both soldiers, struck by the flat of the Sheriff's sword, fell and lay writhing on the ground.

THE SHERIFF: Any questions?

It was then that Sir Ranulf de Pudsey came striding into the yard. A typical nobleman, Sir Ranulf was powerful, stupid, illiterate and dangerous. Imperiously, he said:

SIR RANULF: My Lord Sheriff?

THE SHERIFF: Yes, my Lord?

SIR RANULF: It's time to go.

The Sheriff spoke politely, with perfectly disguised distaste.

THE SHERIFF: Sir Ranulf, never tell me; always ask.

Five minutes later, The Sheriff and Sir Ranulf, followed by four men-at-arms, went riding through the fortress gate, past a group of workmen who were repairing the winch on the portcullis and into the outer courtyard.

The yard was crowded now with townspeople setting up market stalls for the day, and as the Sheriff and his party were riding by, Robin, John and Will and Tuck reined in on a hilltop and looked out across the meadowland.

Ahead of them lay Kirkly Abbey. Poor and small it was; a little place. A low stone wall, a courtyard, a tiny chapel. There was a tower, too, if you could call it that: it rose no more than twenty feet, with wooden stairs outside.

Robin took the abbey in, then veered off to the left of it. Will shook his head.

ROBIN: Kirkly town's off this way.

WILL: Marian's up there.

ROBIN: Up there? That's Kirkly Abbey.

TUCK: So it is.

ROBIN: But what's she doing there?

TUCK: She's lived there now for eighteen years or more.

ROBIN: A nun she can't be, not my Marian. Has she retired from the world, like dried-up gentlewomen do?

WILL: You'll see.

ROBIN: I won't know what to say.

TUCK: She'll think of something.

They started trotting toward the abbey. Marian was busy and she did not see them coming. She was in the little tower, in the room on top. Before her, on an oaken table, were neat rows of jars containing herbs and powders: medicines, which she was mixing in a pestle with great skill.

She was over forty, Marian, and very beautiful. She was both strong and delicate; a woman at the same time indestructible and fragile. Mixing done, she crossed the little room to where an aged peasant woman lay upon a narrow bed. She gently raised the woman's head and said:

MARIAN: This will help the pain.

As the woman drank, a voice came floating through the tower window.

ROBIN'S VOICE: Hello the abbey.

MARIAN: Damn them all to hell.

She was given to swearing and, crossing herself automatically, she murmured:

MARIAN: Forgive me.

Then, bending over the peasant woman:

MARIAN: It's the Sheriff. I've a busy day.

ROBIN'S VOICE: Hello?

Marian, eyes blazing with anger, started for the window. Down below, in the abbey forecourt, Robin called again.

ROBIN: Hello?

Increasingly ill at ease, he turned and said:

ROBIN: Tuck, you go in. I never really said good-bye; she might be angry. Better yet, let's leave it for another day.

He was turning to go when Marian leaned out the tower window.

MARIAN: You there! What in hell do you want?

ROBIN: This *is* Kirkly Abbey?

MARIAN: Right you are and I'm the Abbess. Who are you?

ROBIN: Good God, it's Marian.

MARIAN: Robin?

ROBIN: Marian, what are you doing in that costume?

MARIAN: Living in it.

ROBIN: I've come home to you. The wars are over, Marian. I'm here.

MARIAN: It's Mother Jennet now and you can trot back to Jerusalem.

ROBIN: You're angry.

MARIAN: Not with you. I haven't thought of you in twenty years.

ROBIN: Then smile at me and ask me in.

MARIAN: Come back tomorrow: I'll be gone. The Sheriff's coming for me and I'm off to prison.

Saying which, she withdrew from the window.

ROBIN: Off to prison? Marian?

MARIAN: Oh, damn the man.

She had a lot to do. She left the tower room, went racing down and through the tiny chapel, out

the back and into a little walled garden. In amongst the herbs and vegetables were four young Nuns, all pale and anxious, trying to be busy. They gathered round her as she said:

MARIAN: They'll be here for me soon. You're in no danger from the Sheriff and you're free to carry on. No services, of course, but—

There was a flicker of annoyance on her face as Robin, from inside the chapel, called out:

ROBIN: Marian?

MARIAN: But you must help all those who come as best you can. Don't worry for me, I'll be well—

She broke off, opened up her arms to all four Sisters, hugged them close.

MARIAN: The Lord will keep you.

ROBIN: Marian.

He was in the garden. Marian, with one last squeeze, turned round and started briskly toward him.

ROBIN: What's happening? Explain.

MARIAN: I haven't time.

She whizzed right past him, through the chapel, out the front and along a little row of thatched huts. Robin, several paces to the rear, hurried after her.

ROBIN: What's the Sheriff coming for? What's wrong? What have you done?

MARIAN: God's work; it's what I do these days.

ROBIN: If you're in trouble, I can save you.

MARIAN: I have nothing to be saved from. I don't want you, Robin.

ROBIN: But you've got me.

She stopped at the door to one of the huts, turned and glared at him.

ROBIN: I like the way you look.

MARIAN: That's more than I can say for you.

She hurled open the door and strode in. He followed. The room inside was bare and small: a narrow bed, a chest, a crucifix, a candle, books. She opened the chest and began to take out clothing.

ROBIN: Is this your room? You live in here?

MARIAN: I do.

ROBIN: There's nothing in it.

MARIAN: I have all I need.

ROBIN: I thought I knew you.

She began to pack the clothing—black and white and gray; all clerical.

ROBIN: It's a change from Lincoln green.

MARIAN: Damned right it is; and I'm changed, too. I am an Abbess. I work hard. I've studied herbs and medicines. I till the fields. I love my life. I will not give it up, and when the Sheriff comes—

ROBIN: But what's he coming for?

MARIAN: Because the higher clergy has been ordered out of England by the King and I'm not going. I am staying here and when he comes, he'll damned well find me doing what I do.

ROBIN: You mean to let him take you?

MARIAN: God is with me.

ROBIN: He was with us on crusade: it didn't help.

She was about to answer when they heard John calling from the abbey forecourt.

JOHN: Robin . . .

Robin turned and started for the door.

ROBIN: Stay here.

MARIAN: It's my life, Robin.

ROBIN: You're a fool.

He bounded out, went racing to the forecourt.
John and Will and Tuck were there, eyes out
across the fields.

ROBIN: How many are they?

JOHN: Six.

ROBIN: I like the odds.

They stood there tense and ready as the Sheriff, Sir Ranulf and the four men-at-arms came cantering to the abbey. The Sheriff, in the lead, reined in. Robin stepped forward. For a long time, the two of them looked at each other. Robin was the first to speak. He smiled and bowed.

ROBIN: My Lord Sheriff.

THE SHERIFF: Robin. Still not dead, Robin?

ROBIN: Not from want of trying. You look well, all things considered.

THE SHERIFF: How was the Crusade?

ROBIN: A disappointment. All these years and look at us: I'm nothing but a former captain and you're still the Sheriff.

THE SHERIFF: No advancement. I can read and write: it made me suspect. Not one duke in twenty reads a word.

He turned with great politeness to Sir Ranulf.

THE SHERIFF: Am I correct, my Lord?

SIR RANULF: Books are for clerks.

THE SHERIFF: You see? And how is Mother Jennet? Did you find her changed?

ROBIN: I didn't find her. She's gone off. Two decades and I've missed her by a day.

THE SHERIFF: The lady's gone, you say?

ROBIN: Last night, the sisters tell me.

THE SHERIFF: Odd: I sent her warning and she answered, "Come and take me."

ROBIN: Both of us have come for nothing. So it goes.

Robin shook his head and he was sighing sadly as Marian, a bag with her possessions in one hand, came striding briskly into view.

MARIAN: I'm ready.

ROBIN: Oh, for Christ's sake.

He was glaring at her furiously as Sir Ranulf turned imperiously to the Sheriff.

SIR RANULF: Is this the woman?

THE SHERIFF: Yes, my Lord.

His eyes on Marian, Sir Ranulf said:

SIR RANULF: By my authority as Bailiff to His Majesty the King—

ROBIN: Who is this oaf?

THE SHERIFF: Sir Ranulf de Pudsey.

MARIAN: I'm your prisoner, my Lord.

She was moving toward Sir Ranulf when Robin grabbed her.

ROBIN: Come back here.

MARIAN: Let me go.

SIR RANULF: Release her.

ROBIN: Take her if you can.

Marian was struggling now in Robin's arms. Her voice was fierce.

MARIAN: Grow up.

ROBIN: I'm saving you.

Sir Ranulf wheeled round at the Sheriff.

SIR RANULF: Arrest them all.

THE SHERIFF: We haven't men enough.

SIR RANULF: I'm here. I'll do it.

Sir Ranulf dropped down to the ground and drew his battle sword. John tensed, Will's hand was on his dagger, Marian was struggling furiously.

JOHN: Robin?

ROBIN: Doing fine.

MARIAN: You ox.

Sir Ranulf stood there, sword in hand.

SIR RANULF: In King John's name, I charge you yield.

MARIAN: I'm trying to.

ROBIN: For God's sake, woman—

He never finished. Marian got one hand free and belted him, a clean blow to the nose. It hurt.

MARIAN: There!

JOHN: He's coming, Robin.

And Sir Ranulf was. Sword raised as Robin stood there, furious and blinking from the blow.

SIR RANULF: Give her to me.

ROBIN: Never.

SIR RANULF: You defy me?

In a rage, Sir Ranulf was about to swing when—

ROBIN: Oh, to hell with it. You want her, take her.

With which, he raised Marian high into the air and hurled her at Sir Ranulf. Sir Ranulf did the natural thing: he dropped his sword and caught her. Marian, the wind knocked out of her, lay limply in Sir Ranulf's arms as Robin stepped up to the man and struck him murderously in the face. Then, taking Marian again as Sir Ranulf sagged and fell:

ROBIN: Crazy woman. John?

THE SHERIFF: I warned him not to.

He dismounted and moved to Sir Ranulf, as Robin handed Marian to John.

ROBIN: Gently . . .

THE SHERIFF: Robin? Oaf or not, he serves the King. You're still a free man. You can leave her here and go.

ROBIN: You know I can't.

THE SHERIFF: I say it anyway.

Robin mounted, reached down for Marian. John raised her. She was still unconscious. Robin cradled her in his arms.

THE SHERIFF: I'll have to hunt you now.

ROBIN: Good hunting to you, then.

THE SHERIFF: God help you, Robin.

ROBIN: If He will.

John, Will and Tuck were mounted now. They started off. Then Robin turned back and gravely saluted the Sheriff.

ROBIN: Until the next time.

The Sheriff returned the salute and watched a moment as they rode away. Then, as Sir Ranulf groaned and, in some pain, sat up, the Sheriff knelt down by him.

SIR RANULF: So that's Robin Hood.

The Sheriff nodded. Sir Ranulf wiped the blood from his face.

SIR RANULF: He is a dead man.

The Sheriff's voice was almost rueful as he said:

THE SHERIFF: Yes, but not just anyone's: he's mine.

VII

Together Again

No one said much on the ride to Sherwood. They went slowly. It was afternoon when they got back and John and Will and Tuck dove into the work of setting up the camp. They leveled the tall grass, chopped wood, gathered rushes for bedding.

Marian was leaning back on Robin's Oak. She watched as Robin straightened by the little stream, squeezed water from a kerchief, brought it to her. Every part of her was aching. She was damned if she would let it show. He knelt beside her, handed her the kerchief.

ROBIN: I didn't mean to hurt you.

MARIAN: Nothing hurts.

ROBIN: I couldn't think what else to do.

MARIAN: You could have let them take me.

Robin shook his head and settled next to her.

MARIAN: What now? Am I to be your prisoner here? Is that my fate?

He made no answer. She looked out at the camp.

MARIAN: There's not much left. I wonder if it ever was much, to begin with.

ROBIN: You were glad enough to be here once.

MARIAN: When I was twenty.

ROBIN: I'll keep you out of prison; that much I can do.

MARIAN: It's none of your affair. I don't know how I look to you but I am not your Marian. I can't imagine living in the world again; or even, for a moment, wanting to. Come morning, I am going to the Sheriff.

ROBIN: No, you're not.

MARIAN: How will you stop me? Tie me to the oak?

ROBIN: It's an idea. Why go to prison? Where's the sense? Who would it serve?

MARIAN: There's always God. It's my life, I can spend it as I like. You went crusading, didn't you?

ROBIN: There are some things worth dying for.

MARIAN: They had souls, too, the heathen that you killed. God can't have wanted your Crusade. If I should die in prison, if it comes, it's for a reason. I'll have stood for something—but I didn't take another life to do it.

Her eyes were hard on his and there was derision in her voice as she went on.

MARIAN: What will you do now? Fight the Sheriff and his men? More corpses? Aren't you sick of it?

ROBIN: You ask if—

He broke off, biting back the anger that he felt. It took a moment for the calm to come, and when he spoke his voice was flat and unemotional.

ROBIN: On July the twelfth, 1191, the mighty fortress that was Acre fell to Richard. That's his one great victory in the Holy Land and he was sick in bed and never struck a blow. And on the twentieth of August, John and I, we stood there on the plain outside of town and watched while every Moslem left alive came marching out in chains. King Richard spared the richest to be ransomed. Then he took the strong for slaves. And then he took the children, all the children, and he had them chopped apart. When that was done, he had the mothers killed and then, when everyone was dead—three thousand bodies on the plain—he had them all eviscerated so their guts could be explored for gold and precious stones. The Churchmen on the scene, and there were many, took it for a triumph and a Bishop put his mitre on and led us all in prayer.

There was derision in his voice now, too, as he said:

ROBIN: You ask me if I'm sick of it? You ask—?

He got up and he stood there, staring out across the clearing.

MARIAN: Robin? Forgive me; I was full of pride.

He turned, looked down at her. She held a hand up and he helped her rise. Then slowly, saying nothing, side by side they started walking aimlessly through the tall grass. It was late afternoon, the sky was full of sunset colors. Her eyes moved here and there.

MARIAN: That's where the kitchen was . . . and over there, we stored the ale. And this—

She stopped. Deep in the grass in front of them, there was an outline, a rectangle of crumbled stones.

MARIAN: Was this our house?

He nodded and her smile grew as she remembered things.

MARIAN: As small as that. The door was here. A chest for clothes, a table with a stool. No, two: we had two stools. And rushes on the floor.

She dropped down to her knees, as if to feel the rushes.

MARIAN: And when it rained, the mud came through. I tried so hard to keep it clean.

ROBIN: I was right to love you all those years ago.

MARIAN: It's odd: I know I loved you but I can't remember how it felt or who I was. Of all things, I've found peace most difficult to come by. I suppose I took the Church up out of anger. It's a blur now but I think I thought that, of all men, you'd mind most if I married Jesus. Not a good beginning and for months, when it was time to sleep, I'd think of you. I'd . . .

Her voice trailed off and she leaned back, reclining on the soft grass. She was smiling when she said:

MARIAN: My confessions were the envy of the convent. I said endless prayers, did dreadful penance; nothing helped but time.

Her smile was gone now and her words, though quiet, had the weight of stones.

MARIAN: I have found peace. I do not dream about you, Robin, and I couldn't peel the years back if I wanted to.

ROBIN: I'll see you safely into Nottingham to-morrow.

MARIAN: Good; that's good. I'd like to rest a while.

She stretched out on her back inside the outlines of her little house, eyes on the sunset sky. He turned to go. He took a step or two. Then, turning back, he said:

ROBIN: I never mean to hurt you and it's all I ever do.

MARIAN: You never wrote.

ROBIN: I don't know how.

He paused, then nodded toward the far side of the house.

ROBIN: Our bed was in the other corner.

MARIAN: Yes, I know.

Her eyes, unblinking, looked up at the sunset. Robin slowly turned and walked away.

VIII

The Way to Nottingham

It had been a long night, little sleep, and everything was cold and sodden from the mist. Robin stirred, sat up and looked around. Marian, still in the confines of the little house, lay motionless, eyes closed and wide awake. The others slept. The dawn was gray.

Robin, every move an ache, stood up. He stretched and bent, felt slightly better, jogged in place until the blood began to flow. John, wakened by the jogging, sat bolt upright, groaned—and so the day began.

No one wanted breakfast. Will and Tuck came with the horses. Marian walked slowly over.

ROBIN: Did you sleep well?

She nodded.

MARIAN: And you?

He nodded. Then, there being nothing else to say, he said:

ROBIN: To Nottingham?

MARIAN: The Abbey first. My things got left behind . . .

She smiled at him faintly.

MARIAN: . . . in the confusion.

ROBIN: You'll have to ride with me.

MARIAN: I always did.

He stood there by his horse and made a move to help her mount.

MARIAN: I still know how.

She leaped up gracefully and sat, eyes straight ahead. He mounted up behind her and they left the camp. They all five rode, not saying anything that mattered, through the woods and out across the meadowland toward Kirkly.

Midmorning and the sky was clear as they came trotting up the hill into the abbey forecourt. Marian looked fondly at the place.

MARIAN: I'm going to miss it. I won't be long.

She ducked under the reins, dropped lightly to the ground and was just starting for the abbey doors when they burst open. Out raced the youngest of the nuns—her name was Sister Mary. She came rushing toward them, crying out in great distress.

SISTER MARY: Mother Jennet, Mother Jennet . . .

Marian held out her arms, embraced the girl.

MARIAN: What is it, what's the matter?

SISTER MARY: They've been taken. We were in the garden, where you left us, and the men came, they came in—

ROBIN: The Sheriff and the oaf?

Sister Mary nodded, went on breathlessly.

SISTER MARY: We ran and I ran fastest but they caught the others and they're gone, they took them all away.

MARIAN: It's all right, they'll be back. As soon as I've surrendered, they'll be home again.

ROBIN: You think?

Marian turned toward him, her temper beginning to fray.

MARIAN: If you'd kept out of it, they'd be here now.

ROBIN: You think it's you the Sheriff wants? It's me. It's John and me.

111

He turned to John, eyes glinting with excitement.

ROBIN: He's sitting in his castle, Johnny, waiting for us, daring us to come.

MARIAN: Take me to Nottingham.

ROBIN: Oh, no; not you. We're going in.

MARIAN: I'll walk there if I have to.

He ignored her, turned to Will and Tuck.

ROBIN: Take them back to camp. We'll join you there.

MARIAN: The Sheriff came for me.

ROBIN: You ready, John?

MARIAN: I wish to hell I were a man: I'd knock you down.

ROBIN: Ah, that's my Marian.

He gave her a tremendous smile, kicked in his heels. His horse swerved round, went racing out the abbey gate. John followed, just behind. Marian, still furious, stood watching as they galloped off.

MARIAN: The old fool.

The ride to Nottingham was something. Off they went, full-tilt across the rolling meadowland, past distant farms, and then onto the ancient Roman road. As always, there were scattered travelers: peasants, merchants, clerics.

They were coming round a curve when, on the road ahead, they saw a farmer pulling at an open cart piled high with chickens fluttering in wicker baskets. Robin's face went tight, he dug his heels in, shouted to his horse. They thundered forward toward the cart, straight at it, then went sailing over. John followed, sailed up after Robin, came down cleanly. He was angry, John was, and he shouted.

JOHN: You could have gone around.

ROBIN: I had to try it.

On they raced. They didn't slow down till the merchant came along. He drove a covered cart that clanged and rattled from the pots and metalware he sold.

What happened happened quickly and, three minutes later, Robin and John sat on the driver's seat in merchant's robes, the merchant sat in underclothes, some gold coins in one hand. And moving at a walk now, on they went, their horses tethered to the back of the cart.

Around midday it must have been when, on a hill crest, Robin reined in and they looked ahead.

ROBIN: There she is, John.

JOHN: Nottingham.

IX

To the Rescue

Pans clattering, they drove slowly through the outer gates and into town. The street was narrow, scarcely wider than the wagon; muddy, deeply rutted, filled with dogs and pigs and ragged people. John looked around, eyes brimming at the sight.

JOHN: They haven't changed a thing.

They went on, past the huts that passed for houses, on to where the tiny street opened to the marketplace. Hard times; not much for sale. Small open stalls with cabbages, potatoes, baskets, clay pots, bits of meat, a few sheep in a pen.

Above the marketplace, the inner fortress rose; the massive gate with its portcullis, high stone battlements, the vast church and the Sheriff's castle with its tower.

The Sheriff and Sir Ranulf stood together in the tower, looking out the narrow window at the marketplace below.

SIR RANULF: He'll never come.

THE SHERIFF: I know him. He's a little bit in love with Death. He won't embrace the Reaper but he flirts, he teases. I can wait . . .

He went on looking. waiting, as Robin stopped the wagon near the middle of the marketplace. They looked around, at once both calm and tense, like gamblers at the table.

ROBIN: Do we go in, John?

JOHN: Roam around, see what there is to see?

ROBIN: No harm in that. See anything?

JOHN: Not yet.

ROBIN: He knows we're coming, he'll be watch-
           ing, waiting . . .

JOHN: Not a soldier anyplace.

ROBIN: So far.

JOHN: What now?

ROBIN: We set up shop. You see a table?

John looked around. All the stalls and trestle
tables were taken. All but one. It stood above them,
near the fortress gates. John saw it.

JOHN: Over there.

Robin nodded, flicked the reins. They started
toward the table. The Sheriff still looked down. He
frowned, then sighed. His face relaxed. Softly, he
said:

THE SHERIFF: Ah, Robin.

SIR RANULF: Where? You can't see anything, it's
            just a crowd.

THE SHERIFF: I see a wagon with three horses.
            One to pull. But two to push?

He slowly shook his head.

THE SHERIFF: I'm almost sorry.

Brisk and cold, he turned sharply from the
window. An Officer stood by the door across the
tower room. The Sheriff issued orders.

THE SHERIFF: Now—at once.

The officer turned sharply, hurried out the door.
The Sheriff returned to the window. Down below
him in the marketplace, John was standing by the
vacant table. Robin, grinning, tossed him pots and
pans which John set out as if for sale. Sir Ranulf,
standing by the Sheriff, was impatient.

SIR RANULF: Why not go out and get him?

THE SHERIFF: Why go out when he'll come in?

The Sheriff's eyes moved and he nodded.

THE SHERIFF: Ah—there we are.

He was looking down at the three Sisters who, with a guard, were just moving through a doorway in the castle out to the inner courtyard. The guard gave them a friendly smile as he said:

GUARD:　　It's no good being inside all day long. Walk where you like.

The three of them looked anxiously at one another, then around the inner fortress yard, at all the soldiers lounging, moving aimlessly around. Frightened, staying very close together, they began, like the prisoners they were, to take their exercise.

　　Outside, in the marketplace, there were pots and pans enough out on display. Robin and John, all eyes, were about to move off when an ancient peasant started toward them through the crowd. His name was Jack and he was shouting.

JACK:　　Hey, there! You lads.

Jack—wrinkled, tough and peppery—came up to them. A step behind came his apprentice, a boy of sixteen with an open country face.

JACK:　　You lads can't do that. That's my table.

ROBIN:　　It was empty.

JACK:　　Makes no matter. Mine is mine. Now off with you.

ROBIN:　　I need it. Look, I'll buy it from you.

JACK:　　Not for sale.

ROBIN:　　For Christ's sake—

He broke off, yanked open his purse and handed Jack a coin. Jack blinked at it.

JACK:　　Gold. I never touched a piece of gold.

JOHN:　　Now, go away.

Jack squinted up at Robin, eyes intense.

ROBIN: Will you, for the love of Jesus, go away.

JACK: I'm good at faces and I know you, don't I?

ROBIN: No.

JACK: I could of swore—

Jack shook his head. Something was wrong. He had it.

JACK: That's not your wagon. Fat man, he
         was here all week, from Bristol. Left this
         morning. That's his wagon. Be you
         thieves?

Robin, ready to kill him, thrust his purse out at
him.

ROBIN: Here; have it all.

JACK: Fair's fair and that's too much.

ROBIN: Old man—

He never finished. Something he saw stopped
him cold. Over Jack's head, he could see the fortress
gates. And in the yard, beyond the gates, the
Sisters walked.

ROBIN: John? John, look.

John turned and saw. When he turned back,
Robin was already at the trestle table, loading himself with pots and pans. John nodded, took some
for himself and, like two tradesmen with wares to
sell, they started tensely toward the great gates and
the inner yard.

ROBIN: It's madness, going in there.

JOHN: Makes no sense at all. There's no way
         out except the gate; they'll bang it down
         on us.

ROBIN: They'll keep, the Sisters will. We'll get
         them out another day.

They stood there by the gate. They knew that
going in was all but suicidal. But in they went.
Hawking their wares and moving toward the
Sisters.

ROBIN: Skillets and pipkins, London-made.

JOHN: Fine pots and pans.

ROBIN: A skillet for you, Sisters?

The Sisters stopped and turned. Robin's voice
was low and fast.

ROBIN: There's a wagon in the yard, a red one, just beyond the gate.

FIRST SISTER: I don't think you're supposed to be here.

ROBIN: Can you see it?

SECOND SISTER: We can't buy your skillet, sir; we're prisoners.

ROBIN: Can you see the Goddamn wagon?

THIRD SISTER: You've profaned the Lord's name.

ROBIN: Jesus Christ, get moving. Run.

FIRST SISTER: Who are you?

ROBIN: I'm a Goddamn friend of Mother Jennet and if you're not fast, we're dead.

The Sisters gasped. They understood. They turned and started racing toward the gate. The Sheriff calmly strode out into view. He barked an order to the soldier standing by the winch that operated the portcullis.

THE SHERIFF: Drop it!

SOLDIER: Yessir!

The Sisters were near the gate. Robin and John, eyes on the Sheriff, turned and began to run. The soldier released the winch. Nothing happened.

THE SHERIFF: Cut the rope, for Christ's sake!

The soldier nodded, reaching for his sword. He got it out. He swung, slashing at the rope. The Sisters were through. The portcullis came thundering down. Robin and John, at full speed, went crashing into it.

They staggered back: it hurt. They looked around. Soldiers were streaming into the yard. There was no way out. Only up. Like two great cats, they started climbing the portcullis. There was shouting in the yard; confusion. It was hard to hear the Sheriff.

THE SHERIFF: The battlements! Get up there!

At the top of the portcullis, Robin and John looked up. The narrow battlement that ran along the top of the fortress wall was twenty feet above them. Straight up, twenty feet of stone. They looked at all the men below, then at each other.

No choice; they had to try it. Fingers gouging for purchase, they started to climb. There was so little to hold on to, fingerholds or toeholds. They kept slipping back, barely holding on. Their faces, pale and sweat-drenched, twisted from the effort.

Below, those soldiers who had heard the Sheriff were racing for the stone steps leading to the battlement. They started up. Robin and John were near the top. A few more feet; not far. Gasping, trembling from the effort, one more heave.

They made it, scraping on their bellies, rolling over onto their knees atop the wall. They looked at each other and grinned. They were free and in the clear—and then they heard the sound of heavy feet running on stone.

They turned and looked. The battlement was

narrow, room for only one man at a time. And racing toward them, converging on them from both sides, were soldiers.

ROBIN: I've seen worse.

JOHN: When?

They surged up to their feet, tore off the merchant's robes and drew their swords. Then, back to back, they braced themselves. It started. The battle swords were massive, heavy, swung like clubs; you didn't have to cut your enemy to kill him.

It was man-to-man at first. But every time a soldier fell, there was another in his place. One soldier, screaming, fell into the marketplace where all the crowd stood silently, eyes on the battle up above. Jack stood among them. Suddenly, he sprang to life, shouting to his apprentice, to anyone who would listen.

JACK: That's Robin Hood. I knew him. Not to speak to: I was just a yeoman—but that's Robin! Robin's come back from the dead to save us all and fight against the King!

Another soldier fell; another. John and Robin were exhausted, staggering, gasping for air. The line of enemies seemed endless. There was chaos and confusion in the fortress yard. Only the Sheriff was motionless, quietly watching. Sir Ranulf, near him, at full cry, was shouting to a passing officer.

SIR RANULF: Where in hell are your crossbowmen? Get them out here!

The officer rushed off. Up on the battlement, Robin was near the end of his strength. A soldier came at him. He parried the blow, he fell to one knee. The soldier raised his sword high. Robin twisted, hoping to avoid the blow. It never came. Instead, the soldier stiffened, pivoted and fell. There was an arrow in his back.

Robin scrambled up, looked out into the market-

place. Will was there; and Tuck. With longbows in their hands. They aimed again. Their arrows flew. Another soldier fell.

Marian was near them in the yard; and Sister Mary, too. All Marian could do was stand there, ashen, eyes enormous, looking at the fighting.

MARIAN: Oh, God . . . dear God . . .

Then the three Sisters reached her, tugging at her, pressing through the crowd.

FIRST SISTER: This way. The red. He said the red one.

Marian came to life, rushed to the cart and jumped up on the driver's seat. As the Sisters piled in behind her, Will kept his arrows flying and Tuck lunged to a large hay wagon and began to push it. As other men rushed to him, helping him drag the wagon to the wall, Tuck cried out:

TUCK: Robin! Robin! Jump!

Robin heard. John, too. They scrambled up, then crouched atop the battlement.

ROBIN: Go on!

JOHN: I'll hurt myself.

ROBIN: For Christ's sake—!

He shoved John, sent him flying off the wall, then jumped himself. The two of them came crashing down onto the hay. The wagon collapsed and they came tumbling, hay-covered, to their feet. Marian had the cart moving toward them. They saw her, made it to their horses at the back and bounded up. The crowd parted and Marian, hands on the reins, drove the wagon clattering and careening through the marketplace, down the narrow street, John, Robin, Will and Tuck all cantering behind.

The Sheriff, high up on the fortress wall now,

stood and watched them go. His face showed nothing. Then, he knelt down by the body of one of his soldiers. His voice was low.

THE SHERIFF: I should have taught you better.

He shook his head and looked round at the other bodies.

THE SHERIFF: Two men, for Christ's sake: two old men.

Then, coming sharply to life, he rose up and started giving orders.

THE SHERIFF: See to that one. He's alive. Pick up the limbs. Get spades and bury them.

He was turning when, down below him in the inner yard, he saw Sir Ranulf, mounted and in full armor, and eight armored Knights on horseback. Voice hard and sharp, he shouted:

THE SHERIFF: You there!

Sir Ranulf didn't hear, kept moving toward the gate. The Sheriff pivoted and hurried toward the stairs. Sir Ranulf, moving through the turmoil in the yard, drew up at the portcullis, shouted to a soldier standing by the winch.

SIR RANULF: Raise it! Raise the gate!

The soldier pointed to the severed rope.

SOLDIER: I can't, my Lord.

Sir Ranulf turned as he heard the Sheriff's voice, cold with derision.

THE SHERIFF: I ought to let you go.

SIR RANULF: I'll bring him back.

THE SHERIFF: You'll bring him? You won't even find him, not in Sherwood.

SIR RANULF: I can do it.

THE SHERIFF: In full armor in the woods? You sink to your ass in the bogs. I've gone in after him; I've tried. I never saw his archers; just the arrows in my men.

SIR RANULF: I can get him and you failed and you don't like it.

The Sheriff's only answer was a look of overwhelming scorn. Then, turning to the soldier at the winch, voice calm and colorless, he said:

THE SHERIFF: Lift it, get some men and lift it. Raise the gate.

X

How Robin Was Hunted

The woods rose up, not far ahead. Marian, some color in her cheeks now, urged the horse on as the wagon bounced and clattered over the field. The sun shone down, the land behind was clear: no sign of pursuit.

Robin and Will, riding in the lead, reined in at the forest's edge. They didn't speak, they'd done it all before. Will leapt down, made a fast exchange: his bow and arrows for Robin's hunting horn. Will slung the horn around his neck, picked out a large, tall tree and started climbing.

Robin led the way into the woods. They started down a broad path, took one narrow trail and then another, splashed across a stream, then cut through undergrowth.

Ahead, there was a clearing, a little lake, soft grassy slopes down to the water's edge, green forest all around. Robin, cantering along the shore, reined in, looked back.

John and Tuck came into view and, just behind them, Marian. She had to turn along the shore. The grass was soft. The wagon lurched, then tipped and went careening full tilt toward the water. The horse went splashing in up to its chest. The wagon, half submerged, sank to a stop and Marian slumped forward with a whimper of relief and covered her face with her hands.

Robin took a deep breath, let it slowly out. He was grinning as he turned and trotted back.

ROBIN: She never had a touch for driving.

JOHN: Think they'll come in after us?

ROBIN: We'll hear from Will in good time if
they do.

He dismounted, started wading toward the wagon.
The Sisters, who had rather enjoyed the ride, were
looking at their Mother Jennet with new eyes.

FIRST SISTER: You weren't afraid of anything.

SECOND SISTER: There's not another abbess like
you in the world.

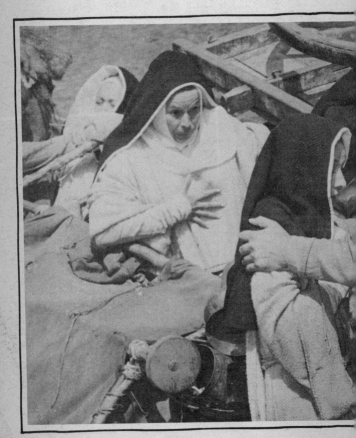

ROBIN: Amen to that. Are you all right?

Her face still covered with her hands, she nodded imperceptibly.

ROBIN: You were a marvel.

MARIAN: Saints do marvels; all I did was . . .

She looked up at him and her voice trailed off. There were bloodstains all over him.

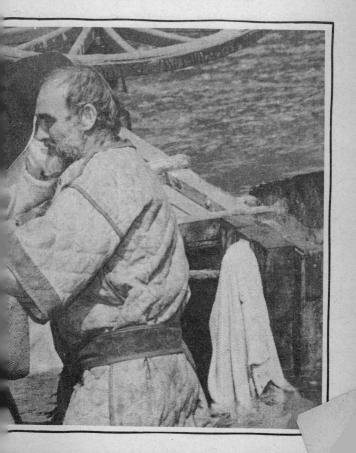

MARIAN: Oh dear God, look at you. The blood;
oh, Robin.

ROBIN: Nothing hurts. I wonder if it's mine.

With which, he dropped into the water like a
stone. He stayed under, blowing bubbles like a boy.
It wasn't easy not to smile, but she didn't. He
came up. Most of the blood was washed away.

ROBIN: How am I?

MARIAN: Don't make a joke of it.

ROBIN: I'm sorry. Can you stand?

MARIAN: I am not altogether sure.

He opened his arms and she slipped off the seat
and into them. Holding her, he turned and started
moving through the clear calm water toward a
grassy slope along the shore. Behind them, as the
Sisters scrambled from the wagon, John and Tuck
began to push it back to dry land.

Robin, in tremendous spirits, lowered Marian
gently to the grass, dropped down beside her. She
looked at him, wavering between smiles and tears.

ROBIN: Was this a morning! Haven't had one
like it since I left.

MARIAN: I haven't either. Did we really do this
sort of thing before?

ROBIN: Oh, all the time.

MARIAN: How did I bear it? Robin, when I looked
and saw you on the wall, I thought I
saw you dead. All stretched out on the
ground and me to mourn you and I
prayed to God—

She corrected herself with a shake of her head.

MARIAN: Prayers are for thanking. What I did
was beg. I begged Him not to let you
die. And here you are. I have more
power than I thought.

ROBIN: What did I ever leave here for?

They neither of them had an answer. Instead, they smiled and she reached out to remove his tunic.

MARIAN: Come, let me look at you.

ROBIN: I'm fine, just bumps and bruises.

MARIAN: All the same.

He shrugged and pulled his tunic off. He sat there bare to the waist in the sunshine. His body was a mass of scars, old battle wounds. She looked at him, then lightly, with a fingertip, began to trace a scar.

MARIAN: Oh. So many. Look at them. You had the sweetest body when you left me. Round you were and hard and not a mark. It felt like silk to touch you. You were mine . . . and when you left, I thought I'd die. I even tried. I walked out in the woods not far from camp and lay down by a stream and cut myself. Some damn fool forester came by, they said, and took me to the abbey.

She shook her head and smiled at him.

MARIAN: No more scars, Robin. It's too much to lose you twice.

ROBIN: I've never kissed a member of the clergy. Would it be a sin?

Her lips moved but she made no sound and they were leaning toward each other when from a distance, faint but high and clear, they heard a hunting horn.

ROBIN: It's Will. They're coming in.

He sprang up to his feet and called out:

ROBIN: John!

He heard it, too. He stood by Tuck. They had the wagon back on shore. Tuck had his bow in hand as Robin bounded up to him and said:

ROBIN: We'll need your bow.

Tuck nodded, handed it to John while Robin picked up Will's bow. Then the quiver, full of arrows. He was about to speak but Marian spoke first.

MARIAN: There's been enough for one day, hasn't there?

Robin looked at her, then turned to Tuck.

ROBIN: We won't be long. We'll meet you back at camp.

MARIAN: For God's sake, Robin, let it be. Don't go.

He had to tell her something. Anything.

ROBIN: It's just to look. I want to see what's hunting me.

She made no answer. Saying more was pointless; so she stood there watching as Robin and John strode toward the trees and, gliding silently among them, disappeared.

XI

How Robin Went Hunting

Will looked down through the leaves. Below, Sir Ranulf and his knights, sun glinting on their armor, went crashing down the path into the forest.

On they went. Now pausing as the path would fork; which narrow branch to take? Now slower, as the woods grew denser and the light dimmed, filtered through the heavy green. Now stopping, listening for the clanging that the cart, with all its pots and pans, would make. Then, hearing nothing, moving on again.

For Robin and John, the woods seemed strange at first. Then more and more, the way was filled with landmarks—fallen trees and bogs and boulders, things they knew. They were moving down a hillside when they heard it. Up ahead. The chink of armor. Then the splash of horses crossing a stream. The splashing went on. The Sheriff, if it was the Sheriff, was moving upstream. They darted forward.

The stream was straight and narrow, all but walled in by the heavy undergrowth. The knights were riding slowly, single file. The last knight was some twenty yards away. His back, his head, his legs were all encased in armor. Only where the calf and thigh plates met was there an opening.

Robin and John stood midstream, side by side. They raised their bows, took aim and shot. The knight screamed as his knees were shattered. He was twisting, falling, as the knight in front of him turned round and raised his visor. One more flight. No scream this time; the knight was dead before he hit the water.

Sir Ranulf came charging to the rear. He reined in where his two knights lay, then raised his eyes

134

and looked downstream. Nothing but empty space:
no one was there.

They couldn't be far. Sir Ranulf listened. Then
he heard. The sounds of men, no telling how
many, racing, crashing through the forest. Sir
Ranulf smiled, called out an order to his men and,
following the sounds, they started slowly through
the woods.

Robin and John were running hard, too hard to
keep it up for long. They didn't have to. It was
there, the clearing was, just like it used to be. Small,
circular, like an arena, walled in by trees. John,
without a word, spun to a large tree and began to
climb while Robin raced across the clearing to the
far side. Then he, too, climbed up and they were
ready, both of them, high up and hidden in the
green when Sir Ranulf appeared.

He stopped at the edge of the clearing, listening. Then he raised his visor, looked around. Cautiously, he started forward, followed by his knights.

Robin waited, let them almost cross the clearing. Then he shot and shot again. A knight fell screaming. Several others turned and started back the way they came. It was John's turn, then. And, from both ends of the clearing, arrows rained.

The knights began to scatter, racing off into the safety of the woods. In a moment, all of them had gone. Except Sir Ranulf. All alone, he circled in the center of the clearing.

It was then that John dropped down and stood there calmly in the open, bow in hand. He took aim as Sir Ranulf set himself to charge.

JOHN: Next time you come to Sherwood, keep your visor down.

ROBIN: No, John! Save him for me.

Sir Ranulf spun around. Robin stood there, just as John did, bow in hand.

SIR RANULF: I hold my office from the King himself.

ROBIN: I never liked your King much.

SIR RANULF: You're his subject and his servant.

ROBIN: He's not King here, not in Sherwood.

SIR RANULF: You're the ruler, are you? Should I bow?

ROBIN: I wouldn't have you in my service. Nobleman. I've met you once, I've known you all my life. You're everything I meant to fight. You are the enemy. You live in castles that we built. You gobble good red meat and we get bread and cheese. You send us off to fight your wars. You own us, work us —Christ, my father worked an honest day for thirty years and left behind an iron pot, a blanket and a spoon. The laws can't touch you, there's no crime you can be punished for and we can shoot a deer and have our eyes put out. I've seen it happen. Even in these woods. No more. These are my woods. I'll live here as I like. If you come in again, I'll kill you.

Robin, scorn and anger on his face, turned away and started through the trees. John followed him. Sir Ranulf made no move. He stood there silently and watched them go.

XII

Was This the Stream?

All of them were working hard. The campsite needed work; on top of which, the time went faster. Will was chopping wood. Tuck, kneeling by the open hearth, had just started a fire and the Sisters clustered around him, shoes and bits of clothing in hand to set out to dry by the flames. The merchant's wagon stood at one edge of the clearing.

Marian, her skirt tucked and her sleeves rolled, was skillfully skinning a rabbit when she heard them coming. She looked across the clearing as Robin and John emerged from the wood. Eyes brimming with relief, she started running toward them.

Robin stopped and smiled. His arms were open to receive her but she pulled up short and stood there glaring at him, scolding.

MARIAN: What took so long? What happened? Was there fighting?

ROBIN: Some.

MARIAN: You promised you were only going to look.

ROBIN: I know, but, Marian, they came in with full armor on.

She blinked at this. She knew the rules as well as anyone.

MARIAN: The Sheriff did?

ROBIN: The oaf.

MARIAN: You didn't kill him?

138

ROBIN: That's for next time. If he comes again.
           I told him . . .

His voice was low, his eyes were locked with hers.

ROBIN: I told the man these were my woods;
           that's all I said. It's all I want. I want
           to live here with you, Marian.

Her lips moved, then stopped; no answer came.
Instead, she turned away and started walking toward the trees. He watched her for a moment, un-
certain what to do. Then, at a distance, moving at
her pace, he followed her.

     She walked, almost drifting, through the trees
and down a slope and on. Not aimlessly; it only
looked that way. For, in a little while, she came
upon a tiny clearing; a patch of meadow grass
dotted with wildflowers, sun and shade. Along
one edge, there was a small stream, running slowly.

     Moving to the stream, she sat, eyes on the water.
Robin saw her sitting there. He hesitated, then he
stopped.

ROBIN: Marian?

She didn't seem to hear him. He went closer.

ROBIN: Was this the stream?

MARIAN: I don't know; possibly. I'm sure of less
           and less as time goes on.

She bent forward, closer to the water.

ROBIN: What are you looking for?

MARIAN: Some trace of Marian or Mother Jennet,
           either one. Good woman, Jennet. Years
           of diligence it took to leave the flesh be-
           hind but she achieved it. She could look
           at men and feel no feeling.

She turned and, looking at him, held her hand
out to him.

MARIAN: See? She looks at you. You want to
           touch her, hold her hand?

He made no move.

MARIAN: It's just as well; she wouldn't feel it.

Her arm was still held out. She turned it, looking at the scar on her wrist.

MARIAN: I think of what I did and can't make sense of it. To want to die from loving you. Some other girl it must have been.

He moved now, sitting down beside her on the grass.

ROBIN: Come let me hold you.

She wound her arms tightly around herself.

MARIAN: There were many women on your great Crusade. Queen Eleanor herself was there a while. And other girls, of other kinds.

ROBIN: Not you.

MARIAN: Why not? Why wasn't I?

ROBIN: Because I loved you.

MARIAN: I am not sure, at this moment, if I want to live or die. Am I old and ugly, Robin? Am I anything you'd want? I've felt so little for so long.

She opened up her arms to him. He bent toward her, gently forward, kissed her cheek. Her arms came tight around him then.

MARIAN: Oh, my sweet Lord. Hurt me, Robin. Make me cry.

He held her and he kissed her and they lay back on the grass and everything was as it used to be.

XIII

 The Merry Men

The woods were dark, the fire glowed. They sat around it, all of them. Will played his lute and sang.

WILL: There's not a lass in all the shire—
    Down-a-down-a-down—
    Whose heart he has not set a-fire—
    Down-a-down-a-down.
    But Robin, everybody knows,
    Loves Marian. To her he goes.
    He takes her by her lily hand,
    He leads her to the forest and
    Beneath the greenwood tree they stand . . .
    And then go down-a-down-a-down,
    And then go down-a-down.

Marian, her head in Robin's lap, looked up at him and smiled. The evening meal had been good; and the wine. Will strummed on softly as she said:

MARIAN: I can't stop smiling.

ROBIN: I don't mind.

MARIAN: Could there be two rooms to our house this time?

He nodded.

MARIAN: And something for a floor?

He nodded again.

MARIAN: I'd like that. And a bed with blankets and a chest for clothes . . .

She paused, looked at her habit, smiled at herself.

MARIAN: I thought I was so happy with no worldly goods. Oh, Robin . . .

She leaned up and they kissed and, in mid-phrase, Will's music stopped. John sat up tensely, eyes out on the darkness. Then, reaching out, his hand on Robin's shoulder, whispering:

JOHN: You hear it?

Robin nodded and his hand moved carefully along the grass to where his sword lay. John, as if stretching, leaned down to the fire where his dagger rested among the dinner bones.

Then, as one man, they both were on their feet, crouching and ready. Tuck was half up, on one knee. Will's knife was in his hand. Silence. Then, from the dark, they heard an old man's voice. Jack's voice.

JACK: Jesus Christ-a-Mighty, don't!

They could just make him out now, edging forward scared to death and blinking at the firelight.

JACK: You do be Robin, don't you?

They grinned, all of them, in relief.

ROBIN: I'll be damned.

JACK: I told 'em in the market it was you.

And turning, he called out into the darkness.

JACK: It's Robin, lads. I told you so.

There was rustling in the dark and then into the firelight they came. Some young, some old, all peasants. It was hard to tell how many; twenty, thirty, maybe more. They stood there silent, frightened and excited, eyes on Robin as Jack spoke.

JACK: I told 'em, "Robin's back in Sherwood," and I led 'em 'cause I knew the way. They all be from the farms nearby but word'll travel and they'll start to come out from the towns now. Out from Not-

tingham and Derby, Blyth and Doncaster. They'll come to serve you, Robin.
For to fight against the King.

Robin turned as Marian moved close to him. She
looked up at him, sad and smiling.

MARIAN: So be it, then. I wanted you all for my
own, the two of us together, nothing
else. But I can't have you that way, can
I? Fight your Sheriffs and your Kings,
I love you and you make me proud. But
if there were a way to turn the clock
five minutes back, I'd give my soul to
do it.

XIV

Enter the King

The tents stretched on and on along the cliff-top, pennants whipping in the wind. The air was chill and damp. The soldiers, shoulders hunched against the day, were busy with the wagons and the horses. Down below the cliff, the gray and angry Channel water frothed against the shore.

Sir Ranulf, weary and begrimed from days of traveling, reined in and looked uncertainly about. He started forward, toward a clump of soldiers nearby, and called out into the wind.

SIR RANULF: You there! Where is the King?

One of the soldiers turned and pointed on ahead.

King John was sitting on his throne—his traveling throne, a solid wooden chair—before the Royal tent. Flags and banners snapped and fluttered in the wind behind him. He was flanked by nobles of the highest rank, one of whom was on one knee in front of him.

John was a stocky, rather handsome man of thirty-five whose face was frank, intelligent and open. He was, like his older brother Richard and the other members of his family, given to fits of uncontrollable rage. He was having one now as, eyes burning, he thundered at the Nobleman who knelt before him.

KING JOHN: . . . so you go to the Goddamn Pope and say if his Goddamn Archbishop puts one Goddamn foot in England, I will cut his Goddamn head off!

NOBLEMAN: Is that all, Your Majesty?

KING JOHN: That's Goddamn all. What's next?

What was next was Isabel, his Queen. She slipped out of the Royal tent behind him, an adorable girl who looked every day of twelve. She wore a soft, voluminous fur cape and nothing whatsoever underneath it. Her voice was soft as she said:

ISABELA: John?

He turned, rage vanishing. The man adored her.

ISABELA: John, aren't you ever coming?

KING JOHN: Soon.

ISABELA: I'm clean all over. Want to look?

She bent close to him, about to open up the cape.

KING JOHN: The whole Court's out here.

ISABELA: I don't mind. I think you're pretty.

KING JOHN: Shhh.

ISABELA: You're pretty everyplace.

He found her irresistible and he leaned up and kissed her lightly as the most important Nobleman present, his Chancellor, cleared his throat.

THE CHANCELLOR: Your Majesty?

Isabela smiled and slipped away, back to the Royal tent. John watched her go and, when he turned, Sir Ranulf was just going to one knee before him.

KING JOHN: Sir Ranulf. What in hell do you want?

SIR RANULF: Men, Your Majesty. Two hundred men.

KING JOHN: Two hundred? What in God's name for?

SIR RANULF: To fight an enemy, my Lord.

KING JOHN: Which one? There are so many.

SIR RANULF: Robin Hood.

KING JOHN: I thought the man was dead.

SIR RANULF: He's back in Sherwood.

KING JOHN: Can't the Sheriff manage it? You take my time about a common thief? My army waits for me in Dover and I'm off to France. Good God, man——

SIR RANULF: But, Your Majesty, the people there, they've made a hero out of him. They're joining him in hundreds.

KING JOHN: Hundreds?!

SIR RANULF: He's a legend. Have you ever tried to fight a legend?

KING JOHN: Just my brother.

SIR RANULF: Sire, they mean to rise against you.

KING JOHN: Do they, do they?

As his rage rose, he rose with it.

KING JOHN: Be in Dover in the morning. I'll give you what men I can. And tell the Sheriff I'll have Robin's head or I'll have his. I want it done! You hear me?

Sir Ranulf heard. He nodded.

XV

They Came, They Saw...

It was a good day, clear and warm, and Robin and John paused at the clearing's edge and looked back at their camp. So much had changed. There were huts and shelters now and Robin's house was all but done. The kitchen, its large open hearth rebuilt, was flanked by trestle tables freshly cut and made. There were a lot of men to feed now. Young and old, all busy. Working, training in the field under Will and Tuck's command.

And Marian was busy, too. There, by the stream, surrounded by the Sisters. They were dyeing bolts of cloth and sewing uniforms of Lincoln green.

They took it all in, liking what they saw, then turned and rode off through the woods. Not going anywhere. Just riding.

The Sheriff, that day, was riding, too. He prayed first, in the fortress's great church. And then, alone, he mounted in the yard, went through the gates, the marketplace, and out into the open countryside.

He cantered down the Roman road, past scattered farms, eyes always on the road ahead. Then, coming to the crest of a high hill, he stopped and smiled wryly.

In the distance, marching toward him in good order, were at least a hundred soldiers: knights, crossbowmen, men on foot. One man rode in the lead: Sir Ranulf. The Sheriff flicked the reins and cantered down the hill.

Sir Ranulf saw him coming and rode out to meet him. Horses lathered, they sat looking coldly at each other, no love lost.

THE SHERIFF: The King was generous.

SIR RANULF: He sends a message. He wants Robin's head.

THE SHERIFF: Or mine?

He smiled and turned his horse off toward the meadowland.

THE SHERIFF: Follow me.

SIR RANULF: These troops were put in my command.

THE SHERIFF: Not in my county. This way.

And not looking back, he trotted off across the grass. Sir Ranulf watched him balefully, about to shout. Then, thinking the better of it, he turned and bellowed toward the line of men.

SIR RANULF: This way!

They left the road and, following the Sheriff, marched across the field. One hour, two; up hills, through streams. The trees of Sherwood rose up on one side. The Sheriff rode on, following the forest's edge, but not too close. Then, when the hill where

Kirkly Abbey stood was visible, perhaps a mile away, the Sheriff stopped. He turned to the men behind and raised his hand.

Robin saw it happen. He and John had seen the troops approaching, and he looked out now from high up in an oak. John stood below him, tense.

JOHN: Robin? How many?

ROBIN: Enough. They've stopped. They're making camp.

JOHN: There in the field?

Robin dropped to the ground and started for his horse. John, at his heels, said:

JOHN: I'd have thought they'd come in after us.

ROBIN: They'll come.

The two men looked at each other, taut with excitement.

ROBIN: Let's go, Johnny.

They mounted and they rode hard, flashing, bounding through the forest. Marian knew at once something had happened as Robin and John came pounding through the trees and cantered to the great Oak. She was moving toward them as Robin bounded down and shouted:

ROBIN: Will! Tuck!

MARIAN: What's wrong?

Will and Tuck were coming up as Robin said:

ROBIN: The Sheriff's out there with an army. Hundred soldiers, maybe more. And good ones, from the look of them.

WILL: Where are they?

ROBIN: Making camp near Kirkly. They should start in after us at dawn. I want us in position by tonight. Get to it.

The rest of the day was a race. The campaign about to start could last for weeks, with Robin and his men fighting, running, hiding, using the terrain and cutting down the Sheriff's forces one by one. Weapons, tools, food and equipment; all this had to be distributed. And not to soldiers or outlaws, but to peasants, farmers and townsfolk who had never known a battle.

It was midafternoon; the men were nearly ready. Marian was in the little house when Robin came. She had clothes of Lincoln green for both of them; rough cloth and shapeless, peasant dress. He took his and began to put it on as she undid her Abbess's robe, white undergarments underneath.

She sat, eyes glowing, watching him. He straightened, gave a sleeve a tug. She smiled and sighed.

MARIAN: Ohhh . . .

ROBIN: I think it fits. What are you grinning at?

She shrugged elaborately, returned to undoing her robe.

ROBIN: I'll help you.

MARIAN: No. I put it on: I take it off. The day I
         wore it for the first time, Mother Joan,
         the Abbess then, good woman . . .

Her robe fell to the floor. Her Lincoln green lay
neatly folded on a little stool. She picked it up,
began to put it on.

MARIAN: . . . I felt such happiness; or so I
         thought. Oh Robin, all I want in all the
         world is living here with you. No show,
         no comfort, just this house. I'd die for
         you, you know. But don't you die for
         me. Not ever.

Her clothes were on. She said it almost shyly:

MARIAN: There. How do I look?

ROBIN: Worth living for.

MARIAN: You soldiers and your soldier's jokes.
The Sheriff has so many men.

ROBIN: I'll come back safe. I always do.

She longed to keep him there, to fold her arms
around him tight. Instead, she reached out and, for
just a moment, touched his cheek.

MARIAN: Sleep well, then.

He looked at her a long time. Then he went.

The men were ready, formed up in the clearing.
They were quiet, all of them; no brave shouts and
no songs. They mutely followed Robin, slipping
off into the woods. Marian, the Sisters near her,
watched them go.

They reached the forest's edge as twilight faded.
All seemed quiet in the Sheriff's camp as they took
up positions for the battle in the morning. John
moved about, inspecting them. All well concealed,
they were.

John nodded a goodnight to Tuck who leaned
against a tree, his quarterstaff in hand. Will, sitting
on the ground and sharpening his dagger, looked
up and smiled as John passed by.

Robin lay out on the meadowland, just beyond
the line of trees, eyes on the Sheriff's camp. Tents
silhouetted against the darkening sky, campfires
burning, men on nightwatch moving back and
forth.

John came and sat beside him. Neither spoke.
Many hours passed before they slept.

XVI

The Sheriff's Move

The dawn was bright. A clear day; beautiful.
The Sheriff's camp looked like a tapestry: tents
neatly pitched with pennants fluttering while horses
grazed and meat was roasted, soldiers moving
quietly, attending to their morning chores.

There was a handsome table set before the
Sheriff's tent. And at it sat the Sheriff, calmly gaz-
ing at his breakfast. Luscious fruit; pears, apples,
berries. He picked up a knife and sliced a pear. It
was delicious.

Robin, high up on a tree limb, watched it all
and shook his head.

ROBIN: Damnedest thing I ever saw.

John, Will and Tuck stood down below, their
heads craned up at Robin.

JOHN: What's he doing now?

ROBIN: Still eating breakfast.

JOHN: Is that all?

ROBIN: That's all.

He bent, then dropped down to the ground beside them.

JOHN: But aren't the soldiers forming up? What
         are they doing out there?

ROBIN: Nothing.

JOHN: What's he waiting for? More men?
         You'd think he had enough. What do
         we do?

ROBIN: We wait and see.

155

And for that day and the next, that's what they did. They waited and they saw. All they saw was more of the same. The horses grazed, the soldiers drilled a bit, the Sheriff ate a long and peaceful dinner and the nightwatch did its watching.

Robin, once night fell, went back to camp. He lay by Marian and talked. She was as mystified as he. And full of hope that there might never be a battle, she curled up in his arms and slept.

He stayed awake a long time, thinking. Finally, the thought came. He knew what to do.

And in the morning he and John and Will and Tuck went out and did it. Mounted, bows and arrows ready, they came charging out onto the meadow from the safety of the woods. Across the

field, a group of knights were idly exercising their horses, trotting peacefully this way and that.

Robin made directly for them, John, Will and Tuck in ragged order just behind. At full gallop, on they went. The knights looked up, reined in— and watched. The Sheriff, by his tent, was watching too.

They were close enough now, well within range. Robin raised his bow; the others did the same. And riding full tilt, aiming as best they could, they sent the arrows off.

One of the knights was struck. Another's horse was hit. The balance of the knights, like dogs on invisible leashes, strained forward, wanting to attack, not moving. Robin, with the others at his heels, was circling toward the woods. He didn't look back till they reined up in the shelter of the trees.

He looked out at the field a long time. Then he nodded slowly, and his face was grim. He understood; it was all clear. He turned—no need to hurry now—and started trotting back to camp. The others followed, full of questions.

Marian was waiting for them. Flooded with relief—they all were safe—she started running toward them. Robin reined in.

MARIAN: What happened?

ROBIN: Nothing.

MARIAN: Nothing?

ROBIN: We attacked but no one followed.

He started to dismount.

JOHN: What's he doing? I don't understand.

ROBIN: He's waiting for us, Johnny.

JOHN: We're supposed to leave the woods and fight him in the open?

ROBIN: That's the plan.

JOHN: But we'd be slaughtered. Does he think we're fools?

ROBIN: It's what he's waiting for: I know it.

JOHN: He's the fool, then. He can wait out there forever. He can't put a forest under siege. He'll either go away or come in after us. If he comes in, we've got him.

ROBIN: Tuck?

TUCK: That's how I see it.

ROBIN: Will?

WILL: If that's his plan, the man's gone mad.

Marian, her eyes on Robin as he nodded, knew what he was thinking. Knew it absolutely and her voice was hard as she said:

MARIAN: You haven't asked me what I think.

He turned to her.

MARIAN: I think one madman is enough.

ROBIN: I know, I know. But Marian, he's out there: he expects me.

MARIAN: Let him.

That was all she said. Two words. With terrible intensity. And then she turned away.

XVII

 The Long Night

Marian lay in the little house. Not sleeping.
Underneath a blanket, eyes wide open, waiting.
Near her head, a candle burned with warm, soft
light.

She heard him coming. Robin's footsteps, just
outside. She sat up and she smiled. She didn't feel
like smiling. Robin stepped into the room.

MARIAN: You look so cold.

ROBIN: The mist is rising.

MARIAN: Come by me.

He paused. Then, moving forward, he sat near
her on the floor.

ROBIN: It's beautiful, this place. The wood,
just now, was full of noises—everything alive—and I kept thinking, I don't
know, of all the death I've seen. I've
rarely lost a battle but I can't think
what I've won. "The day is ours, old
Robin," Richard used to say, and then
it was tomorrow and where did the day
go? Was there ever once a war worth
fighting?

MARIAN: You should know.

ROBIN: They seem worth it at the time. The
King calls and you follow and I swear
to you I've seen God, mounted, in full
armor, on the charger next to me.

He smiled and reached out and touched her cheek.

ROBIN: You are so beautiful.

MARIAN: Tell me a story, Robin.

ROBIN: Now? It's time to sleep.

MARIAN: A battle story. Tell me what it's like to face a man who wants to kill you.

ROBIN: Terrible.

MARIAN: No more than that? There must be more.

He looked at her and shook his head.

MARIAN: Then why go out and meet the Sheriff? You are going, aren't you?

ROBIN: It's a possibility.

MARIAN: You're sure to lose: you must know.

ROBIN: That's another possibility.

MARIAN: You heard what John said, Will and Tuck. They all said it was madness.

ROBIN: Well?

MARIAN: Is that all being dead means? Well? I know there's danger where you are. I live here and I love you and I know it. But why fight when you can't win? Your men: they came to you—oh, God knows why, but being hacked to death for nothing can't have been among the reasons.

Robin paused before he spoke.

ROBIN: Not for nothing.

MARIAN: Then for what? For all the songs about Bold Robin and the glory of it?

ROBIN: You don't think I care for that?

Her voice grew stronger, more intense.

MARIAN: What else? The boys outside? Tomorrow's bodies—is it them you care for?

160

ROBIN: I've never known you to be cruel before.

MARIAN: I'm cruel? I'd go with you, go anywhere, live any way at all, do anything,
be mother, sister, lover for you. I'll do
everything but mourn. I won't. I can't
have found you just to lose you.

ROBIN: I want my life to stand for something.

MARIAN: What does dying stand for?

ROBIN: I'm not dead; not yet. You think I'm
old? Is that it?

She didn't think it, truly not.

MARIAN: No, no—

ROBIN: Gray and old. I'm not. I'm all I ever
was. You saw me on the wall.

MARIAN: And if you do come back, there'll be
another morning, won't there. And another. And each time, you'll be a little
less, not Robin anymore. And one day—

Her voice broke and she closed her eyes. He looked
at her with anger.

ROBIN: You'll see what I can do.

Her eyes flew open, locked with his.

MARIAN: No—I won't see. Or hear. Or think
about it. I'll be gone.

ROBIN: You wouldn't leave me.

MARIAN: All the time you were away, I never
knew, I never heard . . . and look what
happened: you came back. Go fight your
Sheriff and may God go with you, let
the sun shine and the day be great. But,
Robin, I don't ever want to know.

She looked at him for many seconds. Then she
turned away and faced the wall.

XVIII

How Dawn Came

There were no stars. The night was chill, the mist hung windlessly. The Sheriff's camp was quiet. Guards moved slowly and the dogs slept curled up by the night fires.

The mist was heavy in the woods. John stood alone, on guard. He heard sounds, someone moving toward him on the wet grass. He turned and saw. Saw Marian. She hadn't slept and she was stretched tight, close to breaking. She spoke before he could, words coming fast.

MARIAN: John, I'll do anything you say. I'll leave, I'll go as if he never found me, only stop him from this thing.

JOHN: What thing?

MARIAN: Don't let him march you out against the Sheriff.

John looked at her, face blank.

JOHN: What?

MARIAN: He didn't tell you?

JOHN: Fight the Sheriff? Are you sure? It's four to one against us, Knights and, Jesus, we'll be cut to pieces. These are boys we've got, they're farmers.

MARIAN: Tell him. You're the only one, he'll listen. Say you'll stay behind. He needs you, John: he's had you all these years because he needs you.

JOHN: Me?

162

MARIAN: He'd never go without you.

JOHN: Me say no to Robin?

MARIAN: Just this once.

JOHN: We've always been together, almost since I can remember. I'd be nothing if I left him. What would happen to me?

MARIAN: Nothing's going to happen if you stop him.

JOHN: But I've always gone where Robin goes.

MARIAN: You'll lose him if you fight.

JOHN: But if he wants me to . . .

It wasn't going right. She had to make him understand.

MARIAN: You've got your own life. What about yourself?

JOHN: I'm nothing much.

MARIAN: I want him safe, that's all.

He didn't answer. It was hopeless and the anger welled up, things she'd felt for years.

MARIAN: I said I'd leave here. What else do you want from me.

JOHN: I haven't asked for anything.

MARIAN: You never liked me much.

JOHN: You're Robin's lady.

MARIAN: Go on, say it.

She wanted it out in the open, how John hated her, but all he did was look at her with love and gentleness.

JOHN: You're Robin's lady and if you'd been mine, I never would have left you.

MARIAN: Oh.

163

She could not stop the tears. Her fists began to beat against his chest.

MARIAN: Oh, damn you. Damn, you've had him with you, you've had years. I'm going to lose him . . .

JOHN: No, you won't.

She put her arms around him, holding tight.

MARIAN: Oh John, John . . .

JOHN: I'll look after him, I'll keep him safe. Don't cry for Robin. He'll be back.

Gently, as if she were a child, he folded his great arms around her, held her close. The mist was showing signs of drifting now and, up above, the sky was gray with what would soon be dawn.

XIX

Let the Sun Shine and the Day Be Great

The sky was lighter now. John looked around. Some of the men—he could just see them through the mist—were stirring. He would have to get them up soon. Get them up and lead them out. He wanted to see Robin. He was turning, starting for the house, when Robin moved out toward him, buckling on his battle sword. His face looked drawn; he hadn't slept.

ROBIN: We're marching out against them.

JOHN: Yes, I know.

ROBIN: She told you?

John nodded.

ROBIN: Well?

JOHN: She asked me not to go.

He looked at John—and Marian was right about how much he needed him.

ROBIN: I see. And you decided . . . ?

JOHN: It's a mad thing, Robin.

ROBIN: And?

JOHN: I told her you'd be lost without me.

John smiled at Robin, a lopsided smile. They stood there motionless, two men at one with one another. Robin's voice was low and firm and what he said was:

ROBIN: Form them up.

It took a while, not long. Dawn was about to break. The men stood ready, armed with bows and

165

arrows, daggers, cudgels, rakes and pitchforks, anything to fight with.

Marian, the Sisters clustered round her, stood near her house. Her Lincoln green was gone and she was dressed in black again. Her face was drained but calm as Robin moved across the clearing to her. For a moment, neither of them spoke. Then:

MARIAN: Good-bye.

ROBIN: That's all?

MARIAN: God keep you well.

He looked at her, then turned as sharply as a man could turn and strode away. She watched him as he led his men off through the mist.

The sun came up. The day was going to be clear. The sunlight, red and orange, shone down on the Sheriff's camp. All was ready for another day of waiting. Fires burned, meat roasted, horses grazed and soldiers moved about.

The Sheriff came out from his tent to greet the day. He held a dagger in one hand and, using it to shave, was looking out toward Sherwood when he stopped and stood there absolutely still.

Across the meadowland, the morning mist still hung along the forest wall. And moving through it like so many ghosts, strung out in one long thin line, came Robin's men.

There was no emotion on the Sheriff's face: no triumph, no elation, nothing. He carefully replaced his dagger in its sheath and took a deep breath that was curiously like a sigh.

He had no need to issue orders; all his men knew what to do. The whole camp sprang to life. Foot soldiers strapped on their swords, the crossbowmen armed themselves, the Knights stood calmly while their escorts strapped their armor on.

Sir Ranulf, armor gleaming in the sun, was on horse and ready when the Sheriff arrived. Behind them, spread across the field, their forces stood. The Sheriff mounted and looked out toward Sherwood.

From the thin line of Robin's band, two men

came riding forward. John and Robin. Seeing them, the Sheriff nodded curtly to Sir Ranulf and the two of them moved out.

Four men, two pairs, they cantered toward each other, on and on, across the field. Midway, in the center of it all, they met. They sat there looking at each other, Robin and the Sheriff. Then:

ROBIN: I'm here.

THE SHERIFF: I knew you'd come.

ROBIN: Of all men, just for you.

The Sheriff understood.

THE SHERIFF: I know.

ROBIN: I want to settle this with champions.

THE SHERIFF: One of your men, one of mine.

ROBIN: The winner takes the day.

THE SHERIFF: Why should I, Robin? When I have you four to one, why should I make it even?

ROBIN: I'm one champion.

The Sheriff nodded.

THE SHERIFF: Ah: and I'm the other.

ROBIN: If I lose, my men are yours. Without me, they're no trouble to you, they'll go home again.

THE SHERIFF: And if I lose?

ROBIN: Your soldiers leave the field.

The Sheriff turned, looked at Sir Ranulf hard and said:

THE SHERIFF: Those are my orders. Am I clear?

SIR RANULF: I let them go, just march away?

THE SHERIFF: Yes, that's exactly what you do. Now leave the field.

The Sheriff turned dismissively away and started to dismount. Sir Ranulf, longing to object, gave up and galloped off.

John was standing close to Robin, watching him unbuckle his battle sword. He felt torn, pulled apart.

JOHN: I promised I'd watch out for you. I promised her.

ROBIN: She's gone, in any case.

JOHN: I'll kill him, Robin, if you don't.

ROBIN: No; what you do is keep my word.

There was nothing left for them to say or do but hug each other.

ROBIN: I'll see you, Johnny.

John stepped back and stood there, longing not to go.

168

ROBIN: Now, off with you.

John nodded slowly and he went away.

Robin turned and faced the Sheriff. Both men held their battle swords. They stood a moment, yards apart, and then, as was the custom, went down to their knees to pray.

Short prayers. The two men looked up at each other.

THE SHERIFF: God save us, Robin.

ROBIN: If He will.

XX

Swan Songs

Two lines of men, not moving; one along the forest wall, the other up on higher ground. And in between, the field. Some sheep were grazing not far off.

The Sheriff was the first to swing. He was as large a man as Robin and a younger one by several years. His sword was met by Robin's in a graceful parry. It was like a dance, in the beginning, and the two men fought as lions do, with fierceness under beautiful control.

The Sheriff struck and struck again. Each time, the blow was parried, swift and sure. Then Robin swung. The Sheriff moved; moved well but not quite well enough. His arm, the free one, took a glancing blow. Not serious, but blood appeared. A roar went up from Robin's men.

Marian, hands on the reins, craned forward. Was that shouting? Was it real or just imagined? She drove slowly on, the merchant's cart lurching, bouncing through the woods, the Sisters crowded in behind.

Her face was set, determined. Her eyes were steady on the path ahead. She was not going back, she would not see whatever happened, she would never know. And then, it all collapsed.

MARIAN: Oh, damn, damn, damn . . .

She thrust the reins in Sister Mary's hand, dropped lightly to the ground. Without a word or one look back, she started running, racing through the woods.

The fight was even now. Whatever edge that Robin had was gone. Much of the grace had gone,

too. They were winded, both of them, and sweating heavily. They paused. Then Robin swung. His sword met nothing and he was off balance for the Sheriff's blow. He staggered back, a shallow wound across his shoulder.

John watched with growing anguish; Robin had to win soon or he wouldn't win at all. He heard the sound of running, turned, saw Marian as she came darting through the woods. She looked around, saw John, raced to him.

For an instant, she was puzzled; it was not what she expected. Then she saw the champions and she understood.

MARIAN: Oh, God . . .

JOHN: I couldn't stop him.

The balance of the fight was shifting now. The Sheriff, gathering himself, surged forward. Robin

172

held a moment, then began to back away. The Sheriff's eyes were bright. He had his man, he knew it. He stepped back and Robin charged and swung.

The Sheriff merely made a small move to one side and Robin staggered past him, sprawling on the ground. He spun round quickly on the grass but there was no attack. The Sheriff stood still, watching, waiting.

Robin made it to his feet and charged again.

Again the same thing happened. Marian, her face gray, twisted in John's arms, buried her head in his shoulder. It was too terrible to watch—but not watching was even more unbearable. She turned, looked out again.

Robin was on his feet. He found the strength from somewhere and the two men fought, both clumsy now and brutal, like two prehistoric animals.

The ending, when it came, came fast. The Sheriff struck and Robin parried, teetered from the effort.

The Sheriff struck again. His sword went deep in Robin's side. The Sheriff stepped away, as if he could not quite believe what he had done.

Robin stood there, feet apart, refusing to fall down. He shook his head and, half spinning, half falling, whirled around. His sword flashed in the sun, then sank into the Sheriff's chest. Sank deep.

There was, for just an instant, wonder and surprise on the Sheriff's face. And then he crumpled, falling as the life ebbed out of him. Robin fell with him, both of them together on the ground.

John started running forward, Marian a pace behind. Across the field, Sir Ranulf, with a cry of rage, dug in his heels. His mount charged forward. In his hand, he held a mace and chain.

John saw him, saw him coming. Waving Marian back, he raced on toward Robin. As Sir Ranulf galloped on, his men began to follow: mounted Knights, crossbowmen, soldiers streaming down across the field. Tuck saw them coming, turned to Will.

TUCK: Oh, Jesus Christ.

WILL: We've got to get them in the woods.

He turned, he signaled, shouting to the men. Some of them spun around at once and made off to the woods. And others stood there frozen at the sight of all the soldiers charging toward them.

John wasn't sure if Robin was alive or dead. He crouched down by him. Robin moved, then looked at John. John bounded to his feet. Sir Ranulf bore down on him, mace flashing, circling.

John drew his sword and there was murder on his gentle face. He held the sword with both hands, like a quarterstaff. He braced. Sir Ranulf swung the

mace. John caught it on his sword and pivoted. It tore the mace from Sir Ranulf's hand; it tore Sir Ranulf from his saddle.

John was on him like an animal. He swung the mace. Sir Ranulf screamed. John swung again, again, kept swinging, hitting, blind with rage, not knowing when the man was dead. He would have gone on senselessly had not another Knight charged up. John swung, unhorsed the man and bounded toward him.

In the woods, it was a slaughter at the start. The Sheriff's forces thundered in and Robin's men, those with no time to hide, had little chance. Old Jack, crouching down behind a bush, picked up a stone—he had no other weapon—stood and hurled it at a passing knight. He never saw the second knight who, charging up behind him, cut him down.

Will and Tuck, with most of Robin's men, were deeper in the woods. The odds were better there. The Sheriff's men began to fall. Not many, just enough to slow them down, and Will and Tuck kept moving, deeper in, toward safety.

On the field, John looked around. Three knights lay dead. The Sheriff's men, the last of them, were disappearing in the woods. The meadow, suddenly, was very still. John turned to Robin who looked up at him and smiled.

ROBIN: You're a stout lad. What's your name?

JOHN: They call me Little John.

ROBIN: Well met.

He raised one hand. John took it, held it.

ROBIN: Let's see how tall you are.

Holding hard to John's hand, needing all his strength to do it, Robin stood. Marian came running to them. Robin's eyes were filled with wonder and he smiled.

MARIAN: Oh Jesus, look at you.

ROBIN: You came back.

She turned to John.

MARIAN: Can you lift him?

ROBIN: I can walk.

MARIAN: We'll take him to the abbey. All my
         medicines are there.

It was a long walk to the abbey. Robin rested
heavily on John. They crossed the field, passed by
the flock of sheep. An ancient shepherd, leaning
on his staff, looked at them briefly with no interest
whatsoever.

On they went. The sun was high when they
came slowly up the rise, into the abbey forecourt.
Marian moved quickly to the tower, up the wooden
stairs. She opened up the tower door and waited as
John, with heavy steps, half-carried Robin up to
her.

She led the way into the little room. It looked
exactly as it did before; austere and calm and curiously beautiful. She went directly to the table
where her medicines were kept. John, his arms
encircling Robin, helped him to the narrow bed.
Robin smiled in relief and sank back gratefully.
John looked at him a moment and then moved to
Marian. Intent, engrossed in mixing herbs and
powders, she said:

MARIAN: John—if they should follow us . . .

JOHN: I'll wait outside.

He paused. Then, bending closer to her, voice soft:

JOHN: I did my best.

MARIAN: I know.

JOHN: Will he live?

She turned then, with the sweetest, saddest smile,
and stretched up and kissed his cheek. They went

together to the door and, after he was gone, she slipped the great bolts into place. Robin watched her and she went back to the medicines, and he was smiling as he said:

ROBIN: I thought I'd seen the last of you. A woman of your word, you are. I'm glad you came. I wonder where the day went. Vespers it must be. What kind of abbey is this? No one rings the hours.

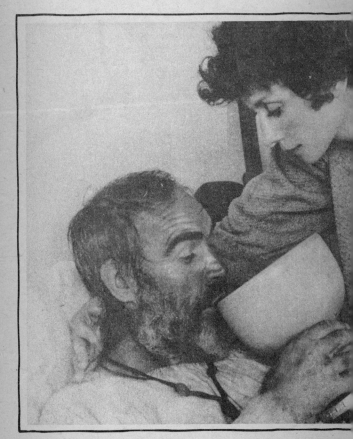

MARIAN: How do you feel?

ROBIN: A little weary. I've had worse; I'll mend.

She added liquid to the powders, mixed it in. She hesitated, frowned, then raised it to her lips and drank of it. She nodded then.

MARIAN: Good; it's good.

She moved across the little space and put the small bowl in his hands.

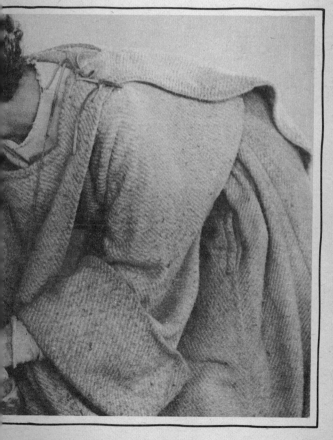

MARIAN: Here: it will help the pain.

He took it from her and his eyes were on hers as he drank.

Outside, below the tower, John was standing, looking out across the fields. No movement, no one in pursuit. He nodded, sighed and, utterly exhausted, sat down to the ground.

The bowl was empty. Robin gave it back to Marian.

ROBIN: He went down well, the Sheriff did. A brave man and the better one, today. The years, the years, they whittle at you. I should give it up, you know. I doubt I'll have a day like this again. And yet . . .

His voice trailed off. He smiled as she sat down by him, gently opening his tunic.

MARIAN: Let's look at you.

ROBIN: He's something, John is. No one's gentler in the world or—did you see him?— half as terrible. I should have gone to tend my men. What must they think? And Will and Tuck; I meant to tell them I was proud. I like your medicine. No pain at all.

She nodded, looking at the deep wound in his side. Then, bending slowly down, she kissed him where the flesh was torn.

ROBIN: We'll have a fine time in the woods. You'll tend me till I'm well again— and then great battles, Marian; great days to come. We'll have a life to sing about.

He broke off talking and he frowned. Something was troubling him. Dead silence. She stood up.

ROBIN: My legs are cold.

She was moving slowly now across the room.

MARIAN: I know.

ROBIN: They're numb.

MARIAN: I said you'd have no pain.

She wavered, leaned her back against the white stone wall. Her legs were numb, too, and she could not stand. She sank down slowly to the floor. He sat bolt upright on the bed.

ROBIN: What have you done?

Her face was ashen and she made no answer. Eyes enormous, full of love, she looked across at him. He cried out:

ROBIN: John!

He looked at her, face tight with rage.

ROBIN: He'll save me.

MARIAN: No one can.

He moved. He tried to stand. His legs were useless. He sank back.

ROBIN: Oh, God.

John was already on his feet. The panic in the cry was unmistakable. He started toward the tower stairs.

Robin shook his head and looked at Marian. The numbness in his legs was rising; nothing hurt. His voice was low now as he said:

ROBIN: How could you do this if you love me?

MARIAN: Love you? More than all you know. I love you more than children, more than fields I've planted with my hands. I love you more than morning prayers or peace or food to eat. I love you more than sunlight, more than flesh or joy or one more day. I love you more than God.

It was all true and he knew it and his eyes filled up with tears.

ROBIN: Oh Jesus, Marian.

He looked away, then back at her again, and what he said was just as true.

ROBIN: I'd not have had a day again to equal this, would I?

She shook her head. He almost smiled.

ROBIN: It's best this way.

She nodded, all strength gone, and leaned her head back, back against the wall. They heard John at the door.

    John shook it. Was it bolted? Why? He couldn't understand. He stepped away, then threw his body at it, crashing. Nothing yielded. He had hurt himself. He didn't know it. He stepped back and charged again. The door shook. He began to sob, he couldn't stop. He shook his head as if to clear it, drew in a great chestful of air and charged again. His mouth was open; he was screaming as he went.

    The door cracked, split wide open. John, half falling, staggered through. He stared about and blinked, his body looking odd, as if his bones were broken.

JOHN: Robin?

ROBIN: Over here.

John turned.

JOHN: Oh Robin, look at you.

He took a step toward Robin. Then he stopped as he saw Marian. She looked at him, dead still, arms folded in her lap. Only her eyes were alive.

JOHN: Oh, no.

ROBIN: It's well, John.

John went to him, knelt down by the bed. There was a look of peace on Robin's face; but not on John's. His hands went out to Robin and he touched him for a moment. Then:

ROBIN: I need my bow, John. And an arrow.

John nodded and he rose and went across the tiny room. Robin turned his head. He looked at Marian. Her hand moved, reaching out for his. He reached out, too. Their fingers nearly touched. John came back with a single arrow and the bow. He stood till Robin noticed him.

ROBIN: Put it in my hands, John. And the arrow.

John did, and Robin fixed the arrow to the bowstring.

ROBIN: Where it falls, John; leave me with my lady. Put us close and leave us there.

His eyes moved one more time to Marian's. They met. And held. And then he pulled the bowstring back and let the arrow loose. It soared up, out the window. Out into the sunlight. Up and up, into the endless blue.

ABOUT THE AUTHOR

JAMES GOLDMAN has won accolades as a playwright, screenwriter, novelist and lyricist. His plays include *They Might Be Giants, The Lion in Winter* and *Blood Sweat and Stanley Poole* (with William Goldman). For the musical stage, he has written *A Family Affair* (with John Kander and William Goldman) and the award-winning *Follies* (with Stephen Sondheim). His adaptation of *The Lion in Winter* for the screen won an Academy Award in 1968 as well as Best Screenplay Awards from the Writers Guild of America and Great Britain. His other films include *They Might Be Giants, Nicholas and Alexandra* and, most recently, *Robin and Marian*. In 1974 James Goldman wrote the bestselling suspense novel *The Man From Greek and Roman*.